# running on empty

## Allie Outram

*Walking Free Publications,*
*West Yorkshire, UK*

# running on empty

*ISBN: 978-0-9549400-1-0*

*First published by:*

Walking Free Publications,
www.walkingfree.org

*Layout & Design by:*

**silverlensmedia**
Copyright silverlensmedia (2008)
Mark van der Wal & Neil Bird
www.silverlensmedia.co.uk

# *contents*

## dedication

# dearest lewis,

I had become the architect of my own demise, constructing my own dark fortress. Your massive heart came to rescue me, and your love has proved bigger and stronger than any of my chains, and has navigated the deep emotional moats surrounding my life. Your love has been brave enough to face off any dragon threatening my heart and break through the isolation of walls I had built to keep others at bay. Your love for me has fought through every barrier and without you I would still be trapped and seeking love and freedom rather than writing about it. Thank you for believing in me, for being my biggest cheerleader, my champion supporter and my greatest fan. I love you, dedicate this book to you, and am so excited about our future together.

# *foreward*

I am privileged to call Allie a friend. She is a lovely, wonderful, bubbly, confident and happy girl. One would need to be very discerning to see any sign of the desperate, destructive journey her life has taken. That journey has been one of both dancing with death and a desperate bid to find freedom from killer eating disorders. Allie's story has to be read to be believed. It is hard to imagine the depths to which she visited the hell of Anorexia Nervosa and Bulimia. She used to look in the mirror and her distorted view saw a huge flabby figure staring back at her. Her face would fill with horror when she saw herself, she detested the sight of her body. She would examine her frame and when she felt the sharp angular bones and taut skin over her body she was reassured, but it was never quite enough. Her weight dropped to under four and a half stone, her shoulder blades and hip bones protruded, her eyes became sunken and her skin turned pale. Her hands and feet were tinged blue and were perpetually cold due to poor circulation. Her arms, legs, back and face began to develop a fine downy hair, her body's attempt to stay warm. Her skin was dry, her hair brittle, it was painful for her to sit on hard surfaces, bed sores developed and as she walked her bony knees rubbed painfully together.

Allie's story has been instrumental in helping me understand eating disorders. You will shed a tear reading her story, you will gasp at the depths of despair she plummeted to. Then you will rejoice with her as her prayers are answered and God reaches down His mighty hand to pull her out of the pit she had fallen into, and set her on a road to freedom. Laughter has returned to her home, God has given Allie the certainty of a healthy, successful and bright future.

*Like the rest of us Allie is still on a journey, with the passing of time she finds new and wonderful levels of freedom. Indeed she will agree with me when I say that she has been given more than she could have ever asked for, thought or even imagined.*

# A wee note from Allie...

Somehow I think that the writer should never appear desperate for the reader to care about her work. It just isn't seemly. She should just do her best and place the result out there. I believe that, but in this case I just can't do it. The contents of these pages are obviously important to me, but I also want them to change your life and give you inspiration.

My reason for writing is to bring a message of hope and healing to people struggling with eating disorders. However, although I'm focussing on eating disorders, you will probably begin to read between the lines that the roots of these problems are universal, and actually relate to a wider range of hungers, drives, addictions, and areas of captivity. Therefore I believe that there is something on the following pages for everyone. My journey to recovery has taken time. It has included agony, sorrow, grief and anguish as I have learnt to expose the vulnerable part of me and face up to the deeper, painful, underlying issues. It was impossible for me to go forward until I was willing to go back. I had reached the point where I had a choice. I could either do nothing, and stay where I was, or I could be willing to face up to the reasons behind my eating disorder and take personal responsibility for my onward journey. The harsh reality is that people who risk nothing, do nothing, have nothing, and end up being a nothing; only a person who risks is free, as the words of the following poem by an unknown author highlight.

"To laugh is to risk appearing the fool.
   To weep is to risk appearing sentimental.
   To reach out for another is to risk involvement.
   To expose your ideas, your dreams before a
   crowd, is to risk their loss.

*To love is to risk not being loved in return.*
    *To live is to risk dying.*
    *To believe is to risk despair.*
    *To try is to risk failure.*

*But risks must be taken, because the greatest*
    *hazard in life is to risk nothing.*
    *The people who risk nothing, do nothing,*
    *have nothing, are nothing.*

*They may avoid suffering and sorrow, but they*
    *cannot learn, feel, change, grow, love, live.*
    *Chained by their attitudes they are slaves; they*
    *have forfeited their freedom.*
    *Only a person who risks is free."*

We are all entrusted with a spotlight, big or small, not to draw attention to ourselves, but to shine the light for someone else. I hope the light begins to shine in your world as you read on.

# chapter 1:

# tuesday's child

"Monday's child is fair of face.
   Tuesday's child is full of grace.
   Wednesday's child is full of woe.

Thursday's child has far to go.
   Friday's child is loving and giving.
   Saturday's child works hard for a living.

But the child that is born on the Sabbath day is
   bonny and wise and good and gay."

*ANON*

### 'I am the product of the family environment'

I was born on Tuesday and, according to the aforementioned poem, I am full of grace. Grace is undeserved favour. It is mercy when we don't expect it or deserve it. In my life, grace has been extended to me in so many ways. Mistakes have been rubbed out rather than rubbed in. In response to this, I want to live up to being Tuesday's child. Grace involves self sacrifice, giving something up in order to give it away. In order to be able to write this book I have had to give up an eating disorder. I now feel qualified to give away a message of freedom to you the reader.

I made a delayed entry into the world. The days were ticking by and I was two weeks past my due date. There was a big thunderstorm one evening and Dad decided to take Mum on a bumpy land-rover ride to see if the jolting would hurry my birth. I think that I was safe and secure in the foetal position in Mum's womb and was reluctant to exit into the daunting and scary unknown territory outside. Maybe I knew about the pain that I was to face and was delaying the inevitable.

However, Dad's little trick worked, I couldn't hide any longer, and on June 14th Alison Catherine Outram was born. Alison is a Scottish name which means noble. Noble can be defined as possessing outstanding qualities, of high birth or exalted rank, and grand or impressive, especially in appearance. Catharine, on the other hand means pure; clean, not contaminated, innocent and free from taint or defilement. It is quite ironic because, due to circumstances and events in my early years, I felt the complete opposite of these definitions. I believed I was inferior rather than superior, had low self esteem rather than inner confidence, and was insecure about my appearance. Also, due to my boundaries being violated, I felt dirtied and unclean. Secrets shrouded my young life like a grey film or clinging residue that refused to be washed off.

I am the product of the family environment into which I was born, coupled with my own individual personality and sensitivities which responded to that environment. My family have been fantastic and I am so grateful to my parents who did the best job raising me. What I write is not meant to dishonour them in any way but I feel it is imperative that I touch on how my upbringing made me feel and how it shaped my beliefs about my value and identity. In reality, my inner self portrait did not begin as a self portrait at all. I inherited my initial perception of my identity from other sources. Beginning with my birth, through childhood and early youth, other people impressed on me certain elements of my identity by the way they treated me and talked to me. In my childish innocence and naïveté, I accepted the portrait that was handed to me. This portrait was not entirely accurate because I was an imperfect person who was raised by imperfect people. My environment lacked an abundance of God's light concerning my true identity so I grew up with a distorted view.

My parent's evaluation of who I was transferred to my impressionable mind as a young child. I saw myself in the light of their prevailing attitudes and actions towards me. Understanding that atmosphere has been a key ingredient in transforming my perception to how God sees me. Consistent, daily parental attitudes and input seem to be more influential in shaping a child's identity than any specific events[3]. Those seemingly small but repeated experiences provided much of the colour to my first inner portrait.

I did not understand that I was unconditionally loved and valued by God because my parents did not display an intimate relationship with Jesus Christ. My Mother and Father do categorize themselves as Christians, but relate to Christ as the head of their religion rather than as a person. Religion implies rules and regulations rather than relationship. I understood that love was conditional and dependent on good behaviour. I worked hard trying to earn my parents' acceptance, affection and approval by trying to be what I perceived they wanted me to be, but I never felt I lived up to the high standards that began as external but were quickly internalized. Despite achieving, I never responded to my triumphs with joy or satisfaction, but with added pressure to continue to succeed at all costs. I was constantly striving and my motivation was fear: fear of rejection and fear of failure or disapproval.

When I was born, my Father was 40 and my maternal Grandpa was 80, so I was very much the precious and long-awaited child and grandchild. My Mum said that it was love at first sight for her. She was a nurse and my father was a teacher. Dad worked at Harrow School and my home was a big boarding house which I shared with 60 boys. As well as the house, I felt that I also shared my Dad too, and I always felt a real distance between us. I'm sure that it didn't help that my Dad's Dad died soon after he was born, so he never had a father figure as a role model as he grew up.

I believe that the mother is the glue who holds a family together but boys are validated by their Dads. A young man needs a Father to endorse him, support him, and help him navigate his way towards manhood. Dad was a terrific sportsman excelling in both tennis and rugby. He played County level tennis, and rugby for the Harlequins Club. As a boy, I'm sure he wished his Dad was sitting proudly in the stands at rugby matches, and applauding his winning shots from the sidelines of the tennis court. A boy loves his Mum's affection, care and comfort, but aches for something deeper she cannot give him which can only come from a masculine, fathering role model[4]. In his book 'The Five Love Languages,' Gary Chapman says that people speak different love languages. The five emotional love languages he describes are physical touch, words of affirmation, quality time, acts of service and giving of gifts[5]. The need to feel loved is a primary human need. Inside every child is an 'emotional tank' waiting to be filled with love. When a child really feels loved, they will develop normally, but when the love tank is empty, due to an inadequate supply of affection, the child will be less emotionally stable. My primary love language is physical touch, with words of affirmation and quality time in joint second place. A tender hug communicates love to any child, but it shouts love to the child whose primary love language is physical touch. Whatever there is of me resides in my body.

To touch my body is to touch me. To withdraw from my body is to distance yourself from me emotionally. Almost instinctively

*'the mother is the glue who holds a family together'*

in a time of crisis, we hug one another because physical touch is a powerful communicator of love. More than anything, I wanted to be hugged and cuddled by my Dad, to spend time with him and be affirmed by him. However, Dad's primary love language was acts of service so he expressed his love for me by being a provider. In order to feel loved I needed to hear loving words and receive tenderness. This need did not diminish as I grew. As a teenager I also felt a terrible loss. I have struggled with a lot of guilt over coming from a 'loving' home, and yet not feeling loved. I know my family loved me, but somehow it didn't feel like the right kind of love. My longing for love was also a longing for safety, protection and intimacy.

Dad was raised to be strong and good, and in his era, the primary way a man showed his strength was in supporting his family financially and practically. Dad did this very well and I am very grateful for this provision. I was blessed with a good education, holidays and 'good report' presents. If I was doing everything right then I received affirmation and praise, however, if I messed up

I met with disapproval, disappointment or 'the look.' Dad withheld the thing I needed the most: himself. He never spoke the words little girls long, no need, to hear. I do not recall my father telling me that I was precious or pretty. I don't remember him saying he loved me and there was little tactility or closeness through physical touch. I don't doubt that he cared for me, but he did not communicate this to me in a love language that I understood.

When I was young, I wanted to be precious to somebody, especially Daddy. I wanted to know that my father cherished me, that I was his baby princess, and that he was my knight in shining armour wanting to protect and spend time with me. I wanted to be so loved, so welcomed, seen, known and treasured. From this place I could become a strong, beautiful and confident woman. I know that Dad was disappointed when I was born because I wasn't a boy. I believe that because of the absence of a fatherly role model Dad didn't really know how to deal with this little girl who was suddenly in his world. Numerous studies have shown that women who report a close and caring relationship with their fathers, who received assurance, enjoyment, and approval from them during childhood suffer less from eating disorders or depression and "developed a strong sense of personal identity and positive self esteem". [6] The environment in which I grew up was very male dominated. I lived in a big boy's boarding house and as Dad's job became more time consuming I felt that he abdicated his role emotionally by elevating his career above me, and I struggled to develop a sense of who I was. My capacity to develop a healthy self portrait was significantly hindered. 'Important' people continually visited our house and we always needed to be on our best behaviour and 'keeping up appearances'. In our family, it was imperative that we looked and acted appropriately. A 'front' was created and outsiders saw and interacted with this 'front', not with what was really happening in the family. This affected my sense of reality and control became imperative to my survival. The only time I was sure that an unspoken rule existed was

*'women with a close relationship with their fathers suffer less from eating disorders or depression'*

when I broke it. I perceived that my value and acceptance were based on performance. When I was diagnosed with my 'psychiatric illness' I felt defective as a person. I think that my 'problem' was brushed under the carpet because of a fear of what the existence of this issue said about us as a family. I carried around hidden shame and developed an obsessional concern for perfection, resulting in low-self esteem.

*'Women learn from their mothers what it means to be a woman, and from their fathers the value they have as a woman'*

This setting was not the soil my soul was able to grow in, and not the garden that my young heart flourished within. Women learn from their mothers what it means to be a woman, and from their fathers the value that a woman has, the value they have as a woman[7]. I spent a lot of my early years wishing I was a boy and envied my younger brother. I was not comfortable in my girl's body and was quite a tomboy. My brother was very skinny and I thought that if I couldn't beat him for my parents' affections I would try to join him.

In order to change my outward appearance, I remember going to bed one evening with a belt so painfully tightly buckled around my waist that it dug deeply into my fragile skin, hoping this would be the catalyst enabling me to wake up the next morning with a boyish thin figure.

I didn't feel a sense of belonging and went through a phase of believing that I was adopted. The fact that I was the only family member with fair curly hair and blue eyes whilst everyone else was dark was further confirmation to me. I felt like a bit of an outsider and misunderstood in many ways. wonder whether my non-verbal cry for help and attention was anorexia? I was beginning to believe that if I faded away people wouldn't notice me so much. I acknowledge that feelings are fickle and that in reality I'm sure I would have been sorely missed, but there was a great disconnect between my head and my heart. My parents were, and still are good role models and moral, law abiding people. They are upstanding members of the community and did their best job bringing me up. I don't doubt that I was quite a handful at times! I wouldn't swap them for the world and am not accusing them for being a trigger cause of my eating disorder. My experiences have moulded and shaped me into the person I am today, contribute to the story I have to tell, and the designer destiny that has been tailor made for me to fulfil.

## *chapter 2:*

# *dignity destroyed*

We all grow up in a world that is at times apathetic and cruel toward us. God loves each of us completely and unconditionally but sometimes people make us feel very unloved. God values us so much that he sent his Son to die for us. The words and actions of others occasionally cause us to view ourselves as worthless and our inner portrait suffers as a result.

As I grew up, my perception of my identity was shaped not only by my parents, but also by several other significant influences. I experienced the horror of being used and then tossed aside. After

*'A trespasser broke in, robbed me of my purity and forced himself into my most intimate place'*

a terrifying incident as a young girl, I trembled under the pain and shame of sexual violation and molestation for many years. I was tormented by the mental replay of being abused and I had no safe haven where I could simply rest and sleep without wrestling images, imaginations, voices and shadows from this dreadful encounter. I was isolated from peace by fear and shame. A stranger trespassed, broke in, robbed me of my purity and forced himself into my most intimate place. Sexual union is meant to be the culmination, celebration, and cementing of two becoming one. It was never meant to be the last act before parting and I was devastated hear the heartless words, "I got what I wanted; now I'm out of here...Oh by the way, thanks."

This extreme magnitude of rejection almost destroyed me. Our wombs were meant for carefully and lovingly planted seeds of life, not for careless ones in the darkness. Our wombs are like gardens and meant to be tended so they can flourish[8]. As women, we were created to be so much more than an outlet of sexual release for men. Men are conquerors by nature, and, as a result of this abuse I felt well and truly conquered. I lost my virginity along with my dignity, honour, strength, self-respect, power, exclusivity, mystery, and innocence. I was left exposed, distrustful and full of guilt and shame. A worm doesn't adequately describe how I felt about myself. A worm can crawl underground and hide without leaving a trail. I identified more with an ugly slug on the patio. Everywhere they go, they leave this horrible trail behind them. I felt like I messed up everything wherever I went. I was living in a man's world and felt my vulnerability as a woman to be a liability. I hated this vulnerability and most of my energy was spent trying to hide my true self, and control my world to have some sense of security.

Anorexia is sometimes associated with a fear of growing up and sexual maturity. I was ashamed of the bodily changes taking place at puberty and, after this experience, wanted to stay as a child rather

*'Anorexia is sometimes associated with a fear of growing up and sexual maturity'*

than become sexual. The idea showing signs of physical maturity, such as fat around the hips and menstruation frightened me. I didn't want the monthly reminder of adult responsibility which would leave me feeling dirty. I was putting off facing womanhood, closing my eyes to my fears, half believing that my sexuality would 'go away.' My friends were confidently growing up and this only served to accentuate my own struggles. Puberty scared me because changes would happen to me over which I had no control over, and my fears drove me to take the drastic measure of starvation.

The crippling effects of my sexual abuse were many. I felt guilty, dirty, disgusted and different. I believed that it was my own desire to be cared for, wanted, hugged and loved which led to the abuse. I felt "deceived by my body; the body was the enemy, and were it not for the body there would never have been a problem."[9] The most powerful emotions I carried around were shame, anger and powerlessness. Shame, because the whole experience had left

*'I felt deceived
by my body'*

me feeling defective. Instead of realising that the abuser had done something wrong, I believed that I deserved to be hurt. Anger was directed towards myself for being such a 'wicked' person who didn't do anything to stop the abuse.

I did not want to face the abuse and my eating disorder helped me cope in various ways with the painful effects. It served as a form of protection. By becoming obsessed with food, what to eat and what not to eat, and by forming a relationship with food, where it, rather than people, brought comfort, I had a greater chance of protecting myself from being wounded by others. Changing my body to be unattractive to the opposite sex also limited my chance of being involved in another unwanted sexual relationship. The pain of sexual abuse felt unbearable and in order to survive, I had to shut down my emotions. Rage, guilt and shame had to be deadened. Self-harm often becomes the only way the survivor knows how to express the horrendous pain when it does emerge. Cutting or burning oneself releases pent-up energy and is a means of making visible what is going on inside. Another way of coping with

**'I didn't want to feel powerless'**

feelings is through overdoses, which are intended to 'kill' the feelings without necessarily killing the person. A survivor may take an overdose in an attempt to 'have a rest' from the conflicts inside, or to express the desire to be protected[10].

By developing an eating disorder, it took the focus away from the real problem. As long as I concentrated on my eating and weight I didn't have time to think about how devastating the abuse was. I was able to escape from confronting a large part of the cause and remain numb, which, at the time, was very appealing. My anorexia, with its accompanying rituals such as compulsive hand washing, extreme tidiness, cleanliness and orderliness, was a way of neutralising the feeling of being dirty. I didn't want to feel powerless again so I took control of my life in the only way I knew how. Having anorexia made me feel special and admired by others, which helped me to feel less worthless as a result of the abuse. However, whilst developing an eating disorder appeared to help me, in the end it brought greater pain. Pushing other people away in order to protect myself only served to isolate me, set me up for crippling loneliness, and reinforced the feeling that I was different and not acceptable. What remained was a terrible inner ache; a silent scream. I eventually had to acknowledge what was causing the torment before I could move forward.

# chapter 3:

# a cry from the heart

"Where is she? I can't find her anymore. Looking into those blue eyes that stare back at me, I am confused. Those eyes are dull, empty of life, the light is gone. Those eyes are not hers. She is hiding deep inside me. And there are so many places for her to disappear. If I lose a few more pounds, maybe she will be easier to find. Without the extra baggage hanging on my body, maybe she will emerge. But that is not the answer. The baggage belongs to her. Suitcases filled with her fears and pain. Wherever she runs and tries to hide, the baggage is her constant companion and continues to haunt her. There is a bottomless *'the end seems so far away and I am growing more and more tired by the minute'*

black hole that threatens to engulf any hope, love, light and fleeting glimpses of freedom and liberation. That light rightfully belongs to her but it has been swallowed up. That light has disappeared from those big blue eyes and has left her in a world of shadows and darkness. Is there a light at the end of the tunnel? The end seems so far away and I am growing more and more tired by the minute. I don't know if I have any energy left to keep fighting. I have come to the end of my own strength, I am fading away and want to disappear. I need some power greater than myself to restore me to sanity. If there is a God out there please help..."

This was a diary entry I found which I wrote when I was 13 and starting my descent into the deadly quicksand that is the hated and tenacious eating disorder anorexia nervosa. Anorexia was not really the problem, but rather a way of coping with a whole series of problems. For some of the aforementioned reasons I felt unsafe, insignificant, and worthless, and I discovered that through not eating and pursuing thinness I was in a better position to handle my world. Life was frightening and full of situations, experiences and responsibilities with which I felt I couldn't cope. All I knew was that if I couldn't control my circumstances then I had to control myself within those circumstances. I was running from life and my anorexia allowed me to temporarily escape pain. When things went wrong, I starved myself and this prevented me from feeling. There was a desperate need to hide the part of myself which had already been, and may continue to be wounded. By withdrawing and concentrating on food and weight I put myself in a position of not forming deep relationships, and reducing the chances of criticism and rejection.

In times of crushing emotional pain, a loss of feeling was very attractive. Not eating produced an addictive 'high', which masked the emptiness. My anorexic behaviour gave me a goal to work towards and it shut my other aches out. Once the pattern set in, other problems appeared to diminish. In the early stages of the illness I had never felt better, I was attaining a level of willpower very few even came near. The lower my weight, the more remote the world seemed. I began to feel numb. I did not have to think about, or cope with, normal experiences and emotions. The only feelings I had were in relation to food and weight. I was like a piece of china, perfectly fragile and something which people would be very careful not to knock or break[11]. My body size represented the way I felt about myself. I viewed myself as so small and insignificant that if existed in a normal body I would rattle around.

My anorexia also provided me with a way of hiding conflict. My behaviour patterns distracted me from confronting my true feelings. I was hurt, disappointed and angry because of what had happened to me, but, because I did not know how to resolve conflict, facing these feelings seemed too dangerous. I tried to disown and destroy them. Blocking off the emotional energy of anger, I became a people pleaser. All my feelings, needs and drives were bound by shame and when the shame had been completely internalized, nothing

'I was hurt, disappointed and angry'

about me felt ok, I felt flawed and inferior. I turned my eyes inwards and scrutinized every minute detail of behaviour and this created a tormenting self-conscience. With parts of me severed and alienated there was a sense of unreality; of never quite belonging.

I was in a great deal of conflict over who I was and where I fitted in with my friends and family. I was at a time in my life when I was questioning my identity, whether I really mattered, and what life was all about. There was an intensity in the questions I was asking myself, and I had a panic-stricken feeling that there were no answers. 'Yes I could damage myself; yes, I could die or do myself irreparable harm, but the alternative was for me to give in and be nothing'[12].

I am a perfectionist and my perfectionism was shown in the high standards I had for myself and in the way I related to others. My determination and drive, which are very strong, can be both positive and negative. Consequently I have achieved well, but when most people would give up I would still be pushing myself, resulting in unnecessary pressure. Being average meant not being good enough and feeling like a nothing. The more I strived to be perfect, the more I felt people would accept me, and acceptance by others was very important. I felt as if every day started at zero. By the end of the day I must have achieved something tangible in order to feel good about myself. And by 'every day,' I meant every single day – workdays, weekends, and holidays. No matter how much I felt I deserved a day of rest, if the day passed without some form of achievement, no matter how small, I would feel dissatisfied. I had an internal fire burning inside of me pushing me to do more and achieve more. After each accomplishment was reached, the fire dwindled for a moment, but very soon it rekindled itself, forcing me toward the next accomplishment. My relentless need for achievement is exhausting and, as an achiever, I must learn to live with a whisper of discontent. However, my drive does have its benefits. It brings me the energy I need to work long hours without burning out. It is the jolt I can always count on to get me started on new tasks and new challenges. It is the power supply that causes me to set the pace and define my levels of productivity. My striving for perfection became concentrated on the body but in reality related to the whole of my life. I pushed myself to excel in both academia and athletics. I was a straight 'A' student, and competed for Great Britain for 10 years in Cross Country, 10km and Half Marathon events. Everything I did needed to be working towards a goal. However, whatever level of perfection I achieved I still lived under a thick cloud of failure. I was afraid of not living up to what I thought was expected of me. There was a constant dread of being discovered not perfect. However low my weight was, it was never low enough because I could still sense that there was an unacceptable part of me needing to be eradicated.

It all began by my carefully controlling what I ate. There were 'acceptable' and 'unacceptable' foods. 'Unacceptable' foods started off as high calorie foods, and later became any carbohydrates or fats, and then anything other than certain vegetables, salads or fruits. Although I declared that I was not hungry, apart from periods of loss of appetite through depression or the effects of

*'Dieting became my whole life... the emptier I felt, the better'*

prolonged starvation, I was very hungry. I felt triumphant in not giving in to the sensation; when I did give in I was filled with self-disgust at my weakness. It was not that I didn't like food, but that I feared losing control and over-indulging. In fact I was fascinated by food and spent hours reading cookery books and preparing meals for other people. There was an intense panic if I ever had to eat more than I had planned. Dieting became my whole life and I dieted to achieve mastery over self. The emptier I felt, the better.

I had a fear of weighing more than a certain weight. I believed in a 'magical' weight at which I considered that everything would be OK. When I achieved this weight and discovered that nothing has changed I set another 'goal'. The pattern continued in an ever downward spiral. I weighed myself frequently; the scales consistently told lies. When I looked in the mirror a huge flabby figure stared back at me and my face, filled with horror, gave away how much I detested the sight. I examined myself with great precision. My hands glided over my body searching for sharp angular bones. As my fingers felt the hardness I was reassured, but it was still not quite good enough.

As my weight dropped, my drooping frame was no more than skin and bone and I barely weighed 4 ½ stone. Shoulder blades and hip bones protruded. My eyes were sunken and my skin pale. My hands and feet felt perpetually cold and appeared slightly purple due to poor circulation. On my arms, legs, back and face I began to develop a fine downy hair, my body's attempt to stay warm. My skin was dry and my hair brittle. My body was frail to hold and it was painful for me to sit on hard surfaces. Bed sores developed and as I walked, I felt my knee bones rub together. My blood pressure was low and my heart rate slow. Despite my physical symptoms I carried my rituals out with determination and I feared that if I let go, I would be faced with a surge of indulgence and agonizing feelings. When people tried to convince me that I was not well I saw it as a threat. Initially I felt superior, as I was able to refuse food when others give in, but

*'It was my way of declaring that I didn't need anything, especially nourishment and people'*

this feeling of superiority rarely lasted. There was still an inner emptiness, a perpetual ache and the awareness of a 'hollow place' somewhere deep inside, the inability to be satisfied.

My triumphant starvation and consequent weight loss was my proof that I was able to exert will-power over the less desirable things in life, such as indulgence and feelings. It was my way of declaring that I didn't need anything, especially nourishment and people. However inside I was crying out for the very things I was rejecting. The irony is that the anorexia, which gave me a sense of power in a life that had known the struggle of powerlessness, ended up in controlling me. The mindset I was in when I wrote the diary entry at the beginning of the chapter was very similar to that of the Psalmist who wrote:

*Oh, God, my Lord, step in;*
    *work a miracle for me—you can do it!*
    *Get me out of here—your love is so great!*


*I'm at the end of my rope, my life in ruins.*
    *I'm fading away to nothing, passing away,*
    *my youth gone, old before my time.*


*I'm weak from hunger and can hardly stand up,*
    *my body a rack of skin and bones.*


*Help me, oh help me, God, my God,*
    *save me through your wonderful love.* [13]

# chapter 4:

# dying on the inside

There was only so long I could starve myself before I was left with a black and white choice between eating or dying. Thankfully I decided on the former, but once I started to eat, the strict control finally broke down and I found myself climbing on board the emotional rollercoaster named bulimia nervosa.

I was trying hard to take control of my life, but was also in a great deal of conflict. I wanted to present myself as someone who was strong, but yet inside I felt needy and emotionally hungry. The conflict 'the little child in me wouldn't allow the adult to grow up'

was in connection with my worth and how I related to others. A socially competent and successful appearance covered up a person full of doubts, inadequacies, fears, aching aloneness and inner isolation. I felt like I was two people: one was capable, strong and intelligent; the other was vulnerable, weak and needing protecting. The little child in me wouldn't allow the adult to grow up, and the adult was desperately trying to be that little child. There was a split between the ferociously independent part of me which was very much in control, and the part which was dependent and struggling to keep afloat. I felt ashamed of the non-coping part of myself and I tried to shut it away from others. The nature of the illness bulimia is one of covering up. It is about hiding the truth, hiding feelings and hiding food. Everything is done in secret; the eating, the vomiting and the tears.

Bulimia felt like being trapped, living in a shell out of which there was no escape. It felt very much as though a monster who had all the control lived inside me. The worse the illness became, the bigger the monster grew, and the greater the fear that one day it may burst out of my skin for the whole world to see. By consuming enormous amounts of food I was saying 'I am desperately needy'. Underneath my façade there existed a hollow aloneness and hunger to be cared for. However, by vomiting the food up I proclaimed 'I reject it all. I am terrified of actually having any of my needs met'. I was afraid that once I allowed people to touch the part of me which longed to be treasured, they would be sucked into my vacuum of hunger. The taking in of food and the vomiting of it out can be understood properly only if these are seen as one unified action. Together they reveal a variety of meanings and represent what is going on in the emotional world of the bulimic.[14]

Maintaining my bulimia took an enormous amount of mental, emotional and physical energy. Energy which would be used to express feelings was used to keep them down. Instead of feeling

*'I reject it all. I am terrified of actually having any of my needs met'*

*'as soon I had eaten I found myself back in touch with my needy, violent, devouring self'*

distress, I felt an uncontrollable appetite. All my bad, needy, unacceptable, angry, hostile, sad and dependent feelings threw me into chaos, and I tried to satisfy myself by cramming food into my mouth. During a binge I would not care what I ate. I would consume other people's left-overs, and even found myself rummaging through dustbins to get my 'fix'. Packets would be ripped open and there was urgency in my eating. It was as though I was wearing blinkers and all I could focus on was my instant gratification and the filling of my painfully empty void.

After my binge I felt heavy, and my poor stomach was so distended I thought it may burst open on occasions. As soon I had eaten I found myself back in touch with my needy, violent, devouring self, and I would be filled with guilt. The anaesthetic had worn off and the agonizing pain resurfaced. I then forced myself to vomit until I was sure that all the evil food had gone and I could return to a comforting state of emptiness. I would feel tired and numb, but relaxed. My bingeing and vomiting concluded with carefully cleaning the bathroom, tidying up and washing myself. Often after this I would collapse exhausted. I must not let anyone know about my dreadful secret. The bathroom was the one place that I would allow my 'mess' to spill over. Just as with the bulimia, when I vomited, created a mess and then tidied up, so in everyday life, once any negative feelings came out or I made a mistake, it was quickly dealt with and no one was any the wiser.

The end result of the bulimia, the eating and the vomiting, is that I felt empty and entirely without needs. This is precisely the feeling I was seeking, and in a limited way, bulimia achieved for me what I wanted. The split-off, unwanted part of myself was contained in the symptom, leaving the rest of my life free from trouble and distress. The problem with this solution is that I had a continual sense of cheating, of achieving everything in a fraudulent way. Everything I actually did was undermined

'the problem with this solution is that I had a continual sense of cheating'

'Eating disorders like anorexia and bulimia offer a false sense of control'

for me by the means I used to achieve it.[15] Bulimia seemed an easy solution at first, if I binged, I purged; if my body repulsed me, I exercised. But those 'solutions' drove me deeper into despair, self-loathing and addiction. Culture and its airbrushed perfection sets an unattainable standard for most, whispering, "If you're unhappy, do something about it." And though the desire for change isn't inherently wrong, focusing entirely on body image can lead to obsession and this took priority over my health, family, and everything else in my life.

As with any addict, it was an obsession that had become my idol. Eating disorders like anorexia and bulimia offer a false sense of control, propelling you into a cycle of disease that robs your self-esteem, disrupts your daily life and affects your health, sometimes to the point of death.

Only by escaping the trap and discovering the beauty inside can you find true contentment. God was issuing me a poetic and classic invitation:

Come, all who are thirsty,
   come to the waters;
   And you who have no money,


Come, buy and eat!
   Come, buy wine and milk
   without money and without cost.


Why spend money on what is not bread,
   and your labour on what does not satisfy
   Listen, listen to me, eat what is good, and your
   soul will delight in the richest of fare . [16]

## chapter 5:

# running from life

A new disorder has begun to emerge, and although it is not yet a recognized diagnosis, it is equally as dangerous as both anorexia and bulimia and carries its own consequences.

This new disorder is called anorexia athletica, or compulsive exercising. A person suffering from anorexia athletica exercises for an amount of time or an intensity that is beyond normal. This person will exercise compulsively in an attempt to control weight in a misguided attempt to gain a sense of power, control, and self-respect.

I had been brought up in a very sporty and active family and excelled in many activities. I represented my Region in both tennis and lacrosse, was a member of all my School sports teams and was voted School Games Captain. I was a good all-rounder. However, when I began restricting my food intake at the onset of anorexia, I also increased my interest and participation in individual fitness activities where I wasn't dependent on anyone else and could control my training. I developed frantic exercise programmes, pushing my body to physical extremes. Exercise involved discipline, and not only kept my weight down, but also rid me of my guilt and helped keep me warmer without eating more. As with fasting, excessive exercise releases endorphins in the brain which caused me to feel 'high'.

*'As with fasting, excessive exercise releases endorphins in the brain which caused me to feel high'*

I gravitated towards long distance running and joined an Athletics Club. I very quickly became successful due to my drive to succeed, steely motivation, uncompromising discipline and ability to push my body to the limit. Within 3 months of starting training I was asked to represent England in a series of races. This was a tremendous honour. I felt a sense of acceptance and belonging and the athletics environment was one in which I could hide and legitimize my eating disordered behaviour. I loved athletics and racing as it allowed me to temporarily escape from myself, but I was really continuing to run from life. I also discovered other individuals in the International circuit who were in the same boat with similar mindsets.

As an athlete with an eating disorder, I was a member of a special population with a special problem. The athlete who has, or is predisposed to have an eating disorder, has difficulties which are complicated by a sport environment that may overemphasize performance, and also demand an ideal body size, shape or weight. This ideal too often involves losing weight or body fat, which can precipitate an eating disorder in an athlete who is predisposed to develop an eating disorder, or it can exacerbate an existing disorder. Additionally, the sport environment may not only precipitate or worsen an eating disorder, it may 'legitimize' it. With its emphasis on a lean body, and through its endorsement of excessive exercise, the athletics environment made it easier for me to be eating disordered, but more difficult for this disorder to be identified and subsequently treated. Additionally, many of the traits that are characteristic of individuals with eating disorders are also characteristics found in good or elite athletes; individuals with eating disorders and good (coachable) athletes are both usually compliant, willing to work hard (even to overwork themselves), perfectionists, able to withstand pain or discomfort, and they have a high need for achievement or superior performance.

*'the athletics environment made it easier for me to be eating disordered'*

As a society, and within the sport community, we have become conditioned to expect certain athletes to have a particular size or shape. For example, sumo wrestlers are huge and basketball players are tall, whereas jockeys are short, distance runners are

'these stereotyped
standards make
it difficult
for observers to
notice when
a particular
athlete has
moved too far'

expected to be thin, and female gymnasts are supposed to be tiny. These stereotyped standards make it difficult for observers to notice when a particular athlete has moved too far in the expected direction in terms of size, shape, or weight. It can be difficult to see a gymnast as too small or a distance runner as too thin. Conversely, however, it is much easier to notice a large gymnast or a heavy distance runner. The exercise component of a particular sport may also attract an at risk individual. Long distance events that required endurance training were attractive to me because I overvalued exercise and used excessive exercise as a means of weight loss or purgation. Outside the sport environment, others criticized me for spending too much time exercising, saying that it took up too much of my time or interfered with more important aspects of my life. However, I was much less likely to be criticized in a sport environment that either implicitly or explicitly communicated the necessity of excessive levels of exercise, and even rewarded it.

I competed at an International level for 8 years as a Junior and a further 4 years as a Senior athlete in Cross Country, track and road events. I achieved a high level of success including a 7th placing whilst running for Great Britain in the World Schools Cross County Championships in China. There were 6 of us in the team and I can confidently say that 4 of us had some form of eating disorder. At this elite level this is quite a shocking statistic but also quite understandable because low body mass, and in particular a low body fat level, are a distinct advantage to performance. The advantages of a low body fat level include physical and mechanical gains due to an increased power to mass ratio, or simply to a reduction in the 'dead weight' that must be moved by the athlete. This is a particular advantage where the athlete has to transport their own body mass over long distances like distance running, triathlon and road cycling.

However, I do know that humans carry body fat for a number of reasons, including to carry on the inherited characteristics of their parents, to provide insulation and protection for their

body and its important organs, to preserve
body hormone levels, and to provide an energy
reserve for the 'lean times'. This last issue is
especially relevant to females, whose gender is
programmed to carry 'hard to shift' body fat on
their buttocks and legs. This may not suit sports
coaches, but it is part of Mother Nature's plan
to ensure that females can support the energy
cost of pregnancy and breastfeeding, come what
may.

I displayed a condition called the Female
Athlete Triad. This syndrome comprises three
distinct medical conditions, disordered eating,
amenorrhea (disturbed menstrual function), and
osteoporosis (low bone density). Due to my large
training volume and low body fat levels I had
been spared the 'curse' and never menstruated.
However, in reality this is not a blessing because
it was a sign that I was not physiologically
healthy. I would love the opportunity to be a
mother some day and hope that I have not done
myself irreversible damage. I have also suffered
from several stress fractures and bone scans have
revealed that my bone density is below what it

*'I didn't respond to my triumphs with joy or satisfaction but with added pressure'*

should be. I enjoyed most of my years of competing, but despite being successful, even to the point of attaining elite status, I didn't respond to my triumphs with joy or satisfaction, but with added pressure, pressure to continue performing at that high level. I constantly questioned my worth and feared that I had little value. I believed that I had to perform well at whatever I did to gain acceptance and approval. My achievement in sport afforded me a small amount of self-esteem which in part motivated me to train and compete harder despite my fatigue, illness and injury; I felt I had no choice. The good feeling I had about my performance tended to be minimal as well as fleeting. Therefore, sport performance became a competition that I couldn't win.

My exercise addiction was very difficult to tackle and admit to because I reasoned that exercise is healthy and beneficial. However, there is a difference between positive and negative exercise addiction. Positive addictions to exercise promote psychological strength and increase life satisfaction and can be used to help people become stronger. These characteristics lead a person toward enhancement of their state of being and functioning. This typically occurs when a person continues to participate in regular physical activity. "With a positive addiction to exercise, exercisers view their involvement in regular physical activity as important to their lives, and they can successfully integrate this activity with other aspects of their lives, including work, family and friends"[17]. Negative exercise addiction, on the other hand, is a psychological and/or physiological dependence on a regular exercise program that is characterized by withdrawal symptoms after 24-36 hours of no exercise. These symptoms may include anxiety, irritability, nervousness, and guilt. Negative addiction to exercise, similar to other addictive processes, is characterized by increasing dose dependence and withdrawal symptoms under deprivation. Deep down I knew that exercise was controlling my life. My day became structured

*'Deep down I knew that exercise was controlling my life'*

in such a way that home, work and relationships took a back seat to exercise. Exercise deterred rather than enhanced my psychological and physiological functioning.

The observation is that exercise addiction is an eating disorder like anorexia or bulimia and is all about control; control over problems and stress at home, work and in relationships.[18] Like other addictions including eating disorders, exercise addiction involves an obsession with thoughts of exercise, use of exercise to escape from undesirable feelings, and dysfunctional reliance on exercise such that the behaviour is continued regardless of the harm done[19]. I was able to recognize my symptoms of negative exercise behaviour but accepting and being able to change them was an entirely different matter. I felt that even though exercise may have controlled my life, it also enhanced my existence. I never felt I could be truly free and if I was addicted to anything then exercise was the lesser of many evils.

Health, fitness and exercise are still important to me and I have to be careful in maintaining balance in this area of my life. However, as my relationship with God has become more important to me I have had the revelation that physical training is of some value, and useful for a little, but spiritual training is useful and of value in everything and in every way, for it holds promise for the present life and also for the life which is to come[20]. My discipline, once exclusively directed to my workouts in the gym, is now also focussed on my walk with God so as to make me fit  both today and forever.

# *chapter 6:*

# *finding God*

An old therapeutic adage says 'The only way out is through'. Life is often unfair. People mistreat us. Good things happen, bad things happen. We all live in a fallen world alongside fallen people with bodies and souls that are tainted by that fallen world. Rarely do we encounter perfection. I have often wondered why God allowed certain things to happen to me but I have heard it said that all suffering is either God sent or God used. All I know is despite the fact I worked unremittingly at my studies and trained incessantly, anything I worked hard to attain ultimately failed to bring me fulfillment and I was continually disappointed in myself. I was conscious of a 'hollow place' somewhere deep inside, the inability to be satisfied. I wasn't aware of it at the time but this

*'I think God was asking me why I was working so hard'*

sense of inner emptiness was the most obvious symptom of a soul in need of God's satisfaction. I think God was asking me why I was working so hard for things that were never enough, could never fill me up and were endlessly insufficient. However, I was not hearing Him. I was easily led into captivity by seeking other answers to needs and desires that only God could meet.

I have spent over 2 years of my life in Inpatient Treatment for the eating disorders mentioned in the previous chapters. I have seen many reputable psychiatrists, psychologists and counsellors. I have done the 12 Step Programme and various addiction treatment therapies. I was very good at talking the talk, but walking the walk was a completely different matter. I externally conformed to the rules and regulations of the hospitals but mere behaviour modification could not bring true change to my life. I cooperated so that I could be discharged from treatment, but I remained the same on the inside.

Treatment mainly concentrated on the physical side and restoration of my weight back to normal healthy range. There was a strong emphasis on food, calories and meeting specified weight targets. However, food is not the issue, just a symptom of the underlying cause. Finding freedom is not about cosmetic change, but about extreme makeover. What I needed was transformation, not modification. I am grateful for the treatment I have received but I was not healed, whole and restored. Doctors can treat people but only the Lord can heal them within and without.

Many of my friends whom I had journeyed alongside during the inpatient process were not cured either, and it looked like we would always have to live with our addictions and manage them. However, slowly a few key people came into my world who had been completely set free from their eating disorders, and they all insisted that it was due to God's intervention in their lives. I so desperately wanted to believe

*'food is not the issue, just a symptom of the underlying cause'*

that freedom could be mine some day, and their encouraging stories inspired me and filled me with renewed hope. They told me that God is no respecter of persons so what He did in their lives He could also do in mine. I was directed to a passage in the Bible where God revealed His plan to change mankind: "I will give you a new heart and put a new spirit within you; I will take a heart of stone out of your flesh and give you a heart of flesh[21]" It was God who was going to pour pure water over me and scrub me clean. He was going to replace my self-willed heart with one that is God-willed.

God is the only one who changes us on the inside. He does not expect us to change ourselves by outward conformity to a set of rules, God changes our desires. I now see that it was all part of God's plan for me to know and understand that secular programmes and treatment centres cannot produce lasting changes in the lives of people. Treatment had focused on my physical and emotional needs but had completely neglected the spiritual component to recovery, which I now see as the most important. Treatment is tending toward a frightening reduction of emotions and, whilst I see a need for anti-depressents in certain cases, I do feel that they are being handed out like smarties. Squelching emotions only stores them in explosive containers. God's Word constantly recognizes our emotional side. No matter how many academic degrees a psychiatrist, psychologist, doctor or counsellor may have, the real power to change a life is in the simplicity of the Gospel of Jesus Christ. God is the only one who can forgive sin, heal broken hearts and restore shattered lives.

*'God whispers in our pleasures, speaks in our conscience, but shouts in our pains: it is His megaphone to rouse a deaf world'*

God awakened an inquisitive questioning in me when He wanted me to go searching for answers. As CS Lewis once wrote, "God whispers in our pleasures, speaks in our conscience, but shouts in our pains: it is His megaphone to rouse a deaf world". By this point God had His megaphone out and I began to hear His call and developed a hunger to find Him. The Great Angler was fishing for my soul. God eventually 'hooked' me and reeled in the line. It was in His perfect timing and He had got me to the right place where I was finally receptive. My once deaf ears could now hear and my once blind eyes could now see the truth.

I became a 'Born again' believer whilst studying at Bristol University. God conveniently placed me in a house with some wonderful Christian friends. I envied their real inner peace and serenity and started asking questions about their faith. At a similar time there was an Alpha Course running at our local Church.[22] Alpha is an opportunity for anyone to explore the Christian faith in a relaxed setting over ten thought-provoking weekly sessions, with a day or weekend away. I found it a safe place to thrash out the meaning of life; to discuss what Christianity really is all about and ask some challenging questions. I felt an unconditional acceptance within the group and a real sense of belonging. I allowed my inquiring mind to investigate the claims of Christianity and had a revelation that it was relevant to my life now. Slowly it dawned on me that my soul hunger, the non-material part of me, was my need for spiritual satisfaction. I prayed for healing and freedom but for me it was going to be a process and a journey rather than a miraculous overnight change. I wanted an instant touch and the easy way out, but God wanted to teach me step by step using each test as a contributory part of

> *'I prayed for healing and freedom but for me it was going to be a process and a journey'*

my testimony. I had found a place of belonging, started believing but the subsequent change in behaviour and finding freedom took a lot longer. I still found myself in captivity with a yoke of slavery strangling my neck. I was a product of my past but was unaware that I did not need to be a prisoner of it.

I had been a Christian for several years but freedom in Christ was not a daily reality for me. I was still in bondage to thought patterns and destructive behaviours. I stumbled across the existence of Mercy Ministries which is a non-profit organization for young women who face life-controlling issues such as eating disorders, self-harming, addictions, depression, suicidal tendencies, unplanned pregnancy and the consequences of abuse[23]. They provide residential programs, free of charge, designed to address the whole person: spiritual, physical and emotional. Their non-conventional approach to the underlying issues changes more than behaviour; the Mercy Ministries program changes hearts and stops destructive cycles. The program includes life-skills training and educational opportunities that help ensure the success of those who graduate. Their goal is to have each young woman not only complete the program but also discover the purpose for her life and bring value to her community as a productive citizen.

At the age of 28, having intermittently battled for 15 years I decided that I would apply for the programme as my last attempt to break free from the addictive chains that bound me. At the end of countless months of waiting, praying, and hanging on to tattered shreds of hope, by God's grace, I was accepted and stayed at Mercy for 6 months. Mercy was a place of support, discipline, and structure; a place full of women who know what it is like to be lost in despair, but having found their own way out, are helping others do the same. I found expert knowledge and understanding and was accepted for who I was rather than for who I could become. It was a challenging time and I know that on occasions I was not a model pupil with a teachable spirit. It is very difficult handing over control of every area of your life and staying within very strict boundaries. I was fiercely independent, set in my ways, selfish, controlling, manipulative and proud, with a difficulty in submitting to authority. The poor staff had their work cut out! The staff at Mercy held a mirror up to me and it was painful to see all my shortcomings, but as it says in the Bible, "Wounds from a sincere friend are better than many kisses from an enemy". [24]

My conscience had become seared and I easily entered into sin without any sense of wrongdoing. After repeatedly making bad choices I become desensitized to the seriousness of my rebellion. The apostle Paul talks about struggling with sin; "I don't understand myself at all, for what I really want to do is the right thing, but I don't do it.

*'scriptures are the red lights on our dashboard. Heed them and safety is ours to enjoy'*

Instead, I do the very thing I hate. I know perfectly well that what I am doing is wrong but I can't help myself because it is the sin inside me that makes me do these things".[25] I had deceived myself by using justification, reasoning, rationalisation, and boundary pushing because I had just enough of the rascal in me to believe that I was the proverbial exception to the rule. However, my secret scamperings did not go unnoticed. God reminded me in His word; "Do not be deceived; God cannot be mocked. A man reaps what he sows".[26] I needed to repair my warning detector and tune it up with a few cautions from Scripture; "Remember, it is a sin to know what you ought to do, and then not do it." [27] These scriptures are inspired by God and tested by time. They are the red lights on our dashboard. Heed them and safety is ours to enjoy.

The concept of an all-knowing, all-powerful God frightened me. I felt intimidated by the thought that someone knows everything I do. What is even more unbelievable is that despite all my flaws and failures God loves me unconditionally, although he is not always pleased with all I do. I was frequently 'disciplined' at Mercy and often felt discouraged and disappointed in myself. However, I was reminded of the following Bible verse: "Every scripture is God breathed and profitable for instruction, for reproof and conviction of sin, for correction of error and discipline in obedience and for training in righteousness"[28] The Lord corrects and disciplines everyone whom He loves.[29]

I now understand that the Lord disciplines us through his written Word, the Bible. As we read it something leaps out at us, shining a light on an area where we have been in disobedience, or where we are not fulfilling God's highest purposes for our lives. God would whisper into my heart over and over again, creating an unrest in me until I did something about it. The more sensitive I become to the Holy Spirit's promptings, the quicker I would act upon the revelation I got. The other way God disciplined me was through a prophetic word that came either directly to me or through the staff. It wasn't a negative or condemning word but something that I just 'knew' was right. I didn't always like what I heard because it challenged my flesh, but there was a knowledge that it was of God. God's motivation in disciplining us is always to take us further on into His purposes for our lives. It is always so that we can have a deeper, more intimate walk with him. His desire is always that we become more free, more passionate about Him and full of life.

The love of God will nourish us - words of his love are vital to sustain our life in Him - but the discipline of the Lord will change us. We must have both, if you only ever listen to the words of love that he speaks then you will be sustained, but very little will be changed radically in your life once you have a revelation of that love. However, when you listen to, and receive God's challenges and disciplining words, you will be changed every single time, and it is one of the quickest ways to grow in God. My time spent at Mercy needed to be a time of change so it also needed to be a time of discipline. A Christian is held captive by anything that hinders the

*'the love of God will sustain us'*

abundant and effective Spirit-filled life that God planned for him or her. I discovered many areas of captivity in my life whilst at Mercy. There were several obstacles which were blocking my access to the benefits that should be the daily experience of every child of God. These included:

+ **UNBELIEF**, which hindered me knowing God, and believing what he said about me;
+ **PRIDE**, which prevented me from glorifying Him;
+ **IDOLATRY**, which kept me from being satisfied with God;
+ **PRAYERLESSNESS**, which blocked my experience of God's peace, and
+ **LEGALISM**, which stopped my enjoyment of God's presence.

In the following chapter I will describe these five obstructions in more detail. As I began to remove them one at a time I found myself experiencing all the benefits that God intended that I should have as his precious, beloved daughter. As I began to believe what God's Word said about me I had a clearer sense of my identity. If you do not know

God, and I'm not talking about a head knowledge but a heart connection, or if you aren't satisfied with Him, experiencing His peace or enjoying His presence, then this may be a possible indicator of some form of captivity in your life and I hope that I can be a contributor to handing you your keys to freedom.

# chapter 7:

# breaking free

Who in his right mind would volunteer to become a slave, chained forever to a life of bondage? Yet that's just what addiction is: self-imposed slavery, selling oneself to a lifetime of bondage to habit or a substance. While we typically think of addiction as a problem related to drugs and alcohol, there are other addictions that can also be destructive. We may become addicted to work, food, exercise, gambling, sex, smoking, addicted to mediocrity, or addicted to an unhealthy lifestyle, procrastination, compulsive helping or co-dependency. We all have our addictions, whether they are 'minor'.

bad habits or dangerous dependencies on substances like alcohol or drugs. One thing we are all dangerously addicted to is sin. We like to do wrong. The only cure, ironically, is to submit to the control of God and his Holy Spirit.

We are still controlled, but his control is always for our benefit and health, not our destruction. God's transforming power is the only thing that can ultimately heal us of all addictions.

I was living an insane life doing the same things, yet expecting different results. I needed to challenge what I did every day that was keeping my eating disorder alive. I had to proactively do something different if I wanted my life to change. I needed to break down old destructive behaviour patterns and build up new and healthy habits.

*'God's transforming power is the only thing that can ultimately heal us of all addictions'*

"I am your greatest helper or your heaviest burden.
   I will push you onward or drag you down
   to failure. Show me exactly how you want
   something done, And after a few lessons I will
   do it automatically.

I am the servant of all great individuals
   And, alas, of all failures as well. Take me, train
   me, be firm with me,   And I will put the world at
   your feet. Be easy with me, and I will destroy you.

Who am I?
   I am a habit!"

'It was time for me to realize the power of habit'

It was time for me to realize the power of habit, take risks and start walking into maturity. I needed to stop waiting and hoping for a miracle cure. Recovery was going to cost me something. I needed to stop seeking the quick fix and going after instant gratification and escapism. "Deferred gratification is the decision to plan your life in such a way that you face and deal with the pain and problems first, in order to experience pleasure more fully later."[30] God wanted me to face pain, not to hurt me, but to set me free. It would have been too much to bear if God was to show me all my issues in one go. He gently and slowly revealed things to me. Slowly I let go and gave Him control of various areas of my life but the grip remained firmly around other areas. I bargained with God, but deep down I knew that this wouldn't work. I was partially obeying Him, deluding myself that this was ok. However, God reminded me that obedience is not true obedience unless it is complete. It is actually disobedience and a form of rebellion. I was exalting my ideas above His and being stubborn. However, the reality was that I was living a miserable, unfulfilled life and would blame God for what was really my own doing. He had given me everything I needed to overcome in life, but it was up to me to use it!

I'm sure that you want to make the freedom Christ promised a reality in your daily life. I certainly did, but I had to address some boulders blocking my access to complete healing, wholeness and restoration. You may be able to identify with some the obstacles I faced which obscured my path and maybe I can give you some tools to use to chip away at them and help you along your journey. Alternatively, you may have no idea that you are in captivity until God begins to set you free. You may be the worst kind of captive: a prisoner unaware. This kind of prisoner is the most vulnerable to their captors, they are the easiest prey there is. If this is the case, I pray that the eyes of your understanding would be enlightened and that God would pry open your comfortably closed mind in the most effective way possible: from the inside out. My major struggles were in the areas of unbelief, pride, idolatry, prayerlessness and legalism.

## Unbelief

My first most obvious obstacle to believing God was unbelief. I didn't have a problem believing in God, but I struggled to believe what He said in His word, and to claim for myself all that He promised me. Why do we have such a difficulty believing that God could love, with the same unfailing love, those we perceive as good and those we perceive as bad? I think it is because we relentlessly insist on trying to humanize God. We tend to love people according to how they act, and we keep trying to recreate God in our image. I know all my bad thoughts, actions and behaviours and find it hard to believe that despite my countless flaws, there is nothing I can do to make God love me more and nothing that I can do to make Him love me less. He may not love all that I do but He loves all that I am.

There is good and bad news involving the issue of a believer's practice of unbelief. The bad news is that unbelief is crippling. The steps we take forward with God we take through faith. Therefore, unbelief literally cripples our spiritual 'walk', casting huge obstacles in the way of a victorious life. However, the good news is that if we are willing to admit our lack of confidence in Him, Christ is more than willing to help us overcome our unbelief. Belief, or faith in the abilities and promises of God, is a vital prerequisite for fleshing out the liberty we've won through Jesus Christ. I tended to run to God for temporary relief but God is looking for people who will walk with Him in steadfast belief. Jesus said "Everything is possible for him who believes". We need to do the possible and trust God to do the impossible.

*'everything is possible for him who believes'*

## Pride

Glorifying God is the second benefit of our relationship with Him. God is glorified in anyone through whom He is allowed to show Himself great or mighty. The primary obstacle hindering this benefit is pride. Pride is a boulder in the road on our journey to freedom. The size of this boulder differs with each of us according to the degree to which we struggle with it. My boulder was far from being a small pebble! Pride can often disguise itself and assume different forms. C.S. Lewis said of pride: "There is no fault of which we are more unconscious in ourselves, and probably conscious of in others, because pride by its very nature is deceitful."

Pride makes us feel special and unique. This statement does not refer to the uniqueness of being created in the image of God; rather, it's the undue self-esteem which makes us feel more important than other people. However, wallowing in self-pity and self-hatred and feeling unworthy is also a form of pride. I know that I have fallen into this bottomless pit by violating the scriptural injunction not to compare myself to others and not believing what God says about me. I am fearfully and wonderfully made by God, but instead I chose to believe lies that I was worthless and insignificant. I have also been guilty of thinking that I was too far gone to save, too wicked and too sinful and this attitude is also a form of pride. I thought that my problem was bigger than God. I was looking at my mountain rather than the mountain maker.

Pride can also lead us to concentrate on our rights instead of our responsibilities and it produces a lack of forgiveness. I know that I have been guilty of saying "Why should I forgive them? They hurt me" and "It wasn't my fault, they started it and everybody else does it." However, many people ruin their health and their lives by being bitter, resentful and unforgiving. I have heard it said that by not forgiving another it is like drinking poison and expecting the other person to die. It is torture to have hateful thoughts toward another person rolling around inside your head. I always looked at forgiving people who wronged me as being really hard. I thought it seemed so unfair for them to receive forgiveness when I had been hurt. I got the pain, and they got freedom without having to pay for the pain they caused. Now I realize that I am helping myself when I choose to forgive. Forgiving does not necessarily mean trusting the

*'now I realize that I am helping myself when I choose to forgive'*

perpetrator again, but it does mean we do not try to get revenge or take care of the situation ourselves. God will deal with those who hurt us if we'll put them in His hands through forgiveness.

I have also displayed the ugly traits of envy and jealousy, both forms of pride. On occasions I haven't rejoiced with others' blessings, but rather concentrated on why I haven't been blessed. Jealousy, comparison and envy are habits that, if left unchecked, will be like parasites eating away at the core of your individuality. God made us distinctive and unique and when we compare ourselves to others, or are envious of another person's life then we are in effect challenging God's handiwork; which is us.

A favourite quote of mine is by Condoleeza Rice who said "It is a dangerous thing to ask why someone else has been given more. It is humbling, and indeed healthy, to ask why you have been given so much."[31] Our default setting is to be self-centred by nature. Learning to love others

*'It is a dangerous thing to ask why someone else has been given more'*

unselfishly is not an easy task. Pride is at the heart of our selfishness; prioritizing our interests over others' needs. We make life so much more complicated when we think life is 'all about me.' The rest of the world never cooperates. No one else got the memo.

When we see ourselves as the centre of the universe, we live in constant frustration because the rest of creation refuses to revolve around us. Life vastly simplifies, and satisfaction greatly amplifies, when we begin to realize our awesome roles. God is God. From our perspective, it's all about Him. Thank goodness, He is the centre of the universe. So how can we live with such a God-centred mentality? Freely! Because from God's perspective, it's all about us. We seek to please Him, He seeks to perfect us, and life works. Not without pain, but with purpose. Without the potter, clay is just dirt. "The Lord God formed the man from the dust of the ground and breathed into his nostrils the breath of life, and man became a living being."[32]

Pride also always wants to be strong. I find it difficult to receive from others or to be vulnerable. Whilst out triathlon training on my bike a few years ago I was hit by a car. I broke my back and pelvis and was in a very bad way My spinal cord was compressed by 50% and I was lucky to be alive. In Intensive Care I was completely dependent on others to have my physical needs met, and was a very frustrated and reluctant patient. I was certainly humbled by the experience as every shred of dignity was stripped away. Everything is either God sent or God used, and while I know He didn't engineer the accident, He certainly used it to teach me a lesson on humility and relying on Him to provide carers to look after me.

God did not design us to boss ourselves. He formed our psyches to require authority, so we'd live in the safety of His careful rule. Satan tries to draw us away from God's authority by making us think we can be our own producer and director. Few things are more contrary to our human natures than desiring anyone's fame

*'God did not design us to boss ourselves'*

above our own. Pride, "the never-failing vice of fools", is a dangerous lure to captivity. To escape, God must empower each of us to roll the boulder of pride off our road to liberty. This stone will roll if we give it three almighty shoves.

*'Pride brings disgrace, breeds quarrels, and points us to destruction'*

The first shove to apply to the stone is to view pride as a vicious enemy. God hates pride and arrogance. Pride brings disgrace, breeds quarrels, and points us to destruction like a compass needle seeking north. The second shove we need to implement is to view humility as a friend. Often our society looks on biblical humility as a sign of weakness. Nothing could be further from the truth. Being filled with pride is easy, it comes naturally. It is our default setting. On the other hand, humility takes a supply of supernatural strength that comes only to those who are strong enough to admit weakness. Our final efforts in removing the stone involve humbling ourselves before God. Humility is not something we have until humbling ourselves is something we do. By humbling ourselves, we are not thinking less of ourselves, but thinking of ourselves less. This step necessitates action before possession. We don't have to hang our heads in self-abasement to humble ourselves. We simply must choose to lower our heads from lofty, inappropriate places, and bow down before God. If we allow God to empower us, the hosts of heaven are sure to hear a thunderous rumble as boulders of pride roll off our road to freedom.

## Idolatry

God wants us to find satisfaction in Him rather than waste our time and effort on things that cannot satisfy. However, when we look to other sources for satisfaction, we are guilty of idolatry.

I believe that God creates and activates a nagging dissatisfaction in every person for an excellent reason. God doesn't want anyone to perish. Rather, He wants everyone to come to repentance. He gave us a will so we could choose whether or not to accept His invitation, but God purposely created us with a need that only He can meet. Anything we try to put in a place where God belongs is an idol. To travel forward on the road to freedom, we must remove the obstacle of

*'anything we try to put in a place where God belongs is an idol'*

idolatry. We begin by recognizing the obstacle as idol worship, but we may find removing it difficult. The first two obstacles to freedom, unbelief and pride, can be removed effectively by a matter of choice; we can choose to believe God, and we can choose to humble ourselves before God. I am not minimizing the difficulty, but I am suggesting that the obstacles are removed by volition. Some of the idols in our lives, things or people we have put in God's place, can take much longer to remove. Some of them have been in those places for years, and only the power of God can make them budge. We must begin to remove idols by choosing to recognize their existence and admitting their inability to keep us satisfied.

The void God created in my life for Himself demanded attention. I looked desperately for something to satisfy me and fill the empty place.

My craving to be filled was so strong that the moment something or someone met my need, I felt an overwhelming temptation to worship it. Whatever we are addicted to is an idol in our lives. For me it was food and exercise and I held onto them with a virtual death grip. I remember the harrowing moment God opened my eyes to see what a lie I had believed. I originally thought that this lie was a good thing. However, I finally allowed Him to peel away my fingers, and I am now trying to keep hold of His grasp only and not slide back into delusion.

Sadly, I often learn things the hard way. Yes, I plunged to the depths before I discovered satisfaction. I am very aware that Satan will constantly try to subtly tempt me down the pathway to destruction. I hope never to forget that I could fall again. Whatever we are gripping to bring us satisfaction is a lie, unless it is Christ. He is the Truth that sets us free. If you are holding anything in your craving for satisfaction right now, would you be willing to acknowledge it as a lie? God does

*'God does not condemn you, He calls you'*

not condemn you, He calls you. Will you open your hand to Him? He is opening His to you. God surpasses our dreams when we reach past our personal plans and agendas to grab the hand of Christ and walk the path He has chosen for us. He is obligated to keep us dissatisfied until we come to Him and His plan for complete satisfaction. God is more concerned with our condition than our comfort and there will be times of temporary discomfort in order to bring about eternal comfort.

## Prayerlessness

The fourth benefit of our relationship with God is to experience His peace. The key to peace is authority, peace is the fruit of an obedient, righteous life. The issue of disobedience and rebellion against the authority of God complicates the life of the captive. I can tell you from personal experience that at times of greatest captivity, I wanted more than anything to be obedient to God. I was miserable in my rebellion and I could not understand why I kept making wrong choices. I have heard insanity described as doing the same thing over and over again and expecting different results and I was definitely engaging in some insane behaviour. Satan had me in such a vicelike grip that I felt powerless to obey, although I wanted to desperately. Of course, I wasn't powerless, but as long as I believed the lie, I behaved accordingly.

Without a doubt, avoiding prayer is a sure prescription for anxiety, a certain way to avoid peace. The Bible says "Do not be anxious about anything, but in everything, by prayer and petition, with thanksgiving, present your requests to God. And the peace of God, which transcends all understanding, will guard your hearts and your minds in Christ Jesus."[33] I would do anything but pray because I wanted something more 'substantial.' Even studying the Bible, going to church, talking to the Pastor, or receiving counsel seemed more tangible. What victory the enemy has in winning us over to prayerlessness! He would rather we do anything than pray. He'd rather see us serve ourselves into the ground, because he knows that we'll eventually grow resentful without prayer. He'd rather see us study the Bible into the wee hours of the morning, because he knows that we'll never have deep understanding and power to live what we've learned

*'prayerless lives are powerless lives, while prayerful lives are powerful lives'*

without prayer. He knows prayerless lives are powerless lives, while prayerful lives are powerful lives.

Prayer is a key ingredient in breaking free. Satan will try to stir up what God wants to skim off. Christ came to set the captive free whereas Satan comes to make the free captive. Christ wants to cut some binding ropes from our lives. Satan will want to use them to tie us in knots. Prayer matters. The Spirit of God released through our prayers and the prayers of others turns cowards into conquerors, chaos into calm, cries into comfort. I put my hand up and admit that I am often the first to turn to others for advice and support but God encourages us to go to the throne before the phone!

## Legalism

As I have previously mentioned, many situations or conditions can keep us from truly enjoying God's presence. For instance, not spending adequate time with Him will greatly affect our pure enjoyment of His presence. Having an underdeveloped prayer life will also rob our joy, as could harbouring bitterness or anger at another person. But the person who studies God's word in depth and experiences a consistent lack of enjoyment often suffers from a condition with an ugly name, legalism. We cannot please God or find freedom in rule-keeping. We never have and never will. Tragically, self-generated righteousness will always appeal to the human heart. Legalism can result when regulations replace relationship, microscopes replace mirrors and performance replaces passion.

'the obstacles of unbelief, pride, idolatry, prayerlessness and legalism need not be a daily reality'

If you can identify with any of the aforementioned boulders that may be obscuring the road to freedom remember that God's specialty is rolling away a stone. The obstacles of unbelief, pride, idolatry, prayerlessness and legalism need not be a daily reality. If you are still having trouble budging one or two of them then show God which one is causing you trouble, put your hands on top of His, and on the count of three…

# chapter 8:

# fun, free, fearless, fighting females

The thief comes only in order to steal and kill and destroy.[34] Have you ever had anything stolen from you? Even if you replaced the article that was stolen, it was probably a trying experience. However, as difficult as that might have felt, Satan - the thief - wants to do even more damage in your life. He does not want to steal your material

**'we must depend on God's strength and use every piece of his armour'**

possessions, he wants to rob you of the joy, peace and hope that you have found in God. He is very subtle and more cunning than a fox who has been made Professor of Cunning at the University of Cunning! (Blackadder). The enemy is devious and crafty. He does not dress up in a devil's outfit with horns and a pitch fork. No, he is much more sly and clever with his attacks. He knows exactly where your individual weak spot is and will go for the jugular every time. He knows firsthand the battles we are experiencing, and he is willing and able to help us in our struggles. In the Christian life we fight against evil rulers and authorities of the unseen world (the powerful evil forces of fallen angels headed by Satan, who is a vicious fighter)[35]. To withstand their attacks, we must depend on God's strength and use every piece of his armour[36]. It helps if we are aware of where the devil focuses his temptations. He tends to concentrate on our physical needs and desires, possessions and power, pride.

As a woman, the chances are that you are dissatisfied with your appearance and this is a potential area where the devil may attack. Therefore you need to know what God says about you and become media savvy. Today we can be whatever we want to be, any dream can be accomplished as long as we pursue it. We have economic security and we live in a relatively peaceful and prosperous nation. We live in the land of opportunity, rich with culture and diversity, the land of the free! The question I pose is, "is it really the land of the free, especially for women?" With all the freedom and prosperity we enjoy, women still remain prisoners. Women are enslaved to a beauty myth, chained to the false belief that our value is based on our appearance alone. In some cases we are we dieting ourselves to death, literally dying to fit in.

Whilst I do not blame the media for causing eating disorders, it is certainly a perpetuating factor in contributing to our discontentment about our body weight and shape. We are

*'is it really the land of the free, especially for women?'*

bombarded with constant, subtle attacks on our bodies. These attacks wear us down and shake our confidence and esteem. We loose our sense of self and individuality and fall victim to the narrow definitions of beauty defined by the media. The media acts as a propaganda machine determined to remind us we aren't good enough, we haven't made it, that we just simply do not measure up.

We learn that our self worth is measured by external factors - by numbers on a scale. There has been a worrying increase in diets and cosmetic surgery, which pose health risks. Why is the media bent on making us feel so down about ourselves? Why do they go to such lengths to make us feel "less than?" The answer is quite simple - pure economics. The media machine is economically driven as billions are spent on items such as cosmetics, new diets and clothes. This "beautifying" empire is dependent on our disempowerment. They count on us buying into their myths and misrepresentations: "We will never fit it, we can never be happy, thus we can never end the pursuit." Alas, the pursuit is endless, the products are endless, the damage to our self-esteem is endless, and the body hatred created is devastating. The assault of unrelenting and air-brushed pictures are everywhere. There is a subtle, continuous bombardment of images of beauty, images defined by profiteers, images that are not real, not authentic, and not attainable.

> 'the assault of unrelenting and air—brushed pictures are everywhere'

The impact that these images have on women is profound. The financial, social and psychological and physical damages of a woman's lifetime pursuit of thinness are impossible to measure. Depression, despair, depletion of self-esteem, the withering and wasting away of physical, psychological and financial resources are unbelievable. We need to begin to make changes and take a personal inventory of how our lives have been impacted by these images and how we have fallen victim to these lies and misrepresentations of beauty. By examining how these images have impacted your life you are better equipped to avoid falling victim to these

**'As a prisoner I had to ask myself some tough questions'**

myths. You will learn to measure yourself by intrinsic qualities that are of far greater value and are far more beautiful than any image manufactured on a movie screen.

As I have previously mentioned, I was a victim of these attacks on esteem, on women's power, on our self-worth. I was a prisoner and almost a casualty of this war. I have now examined my value system so that I do not continue to sink into the prison of repeat diets, repeat failure and lifelong contempt for my body. As a prisoner I had to ask myself some tough questions: when did I start to hate my body so much? When did I begin to measure my self-worth by numbers on a scale? When did I fall prey to the idea that beauty is external and success is measured by factors that have little to do with personal strength and spirit? We must be aware of the images presented to us and unmask these images for what they truly are, destructive, superficial and unattainable images. These images do not value our uniqueness, they do not honour our wisdom and our spirit, and they do not measure us. We must reclaim and redefine our bodies as ours. They are miraculous and our bodies perform wonderful feats every day. We are physiological and biological masterpieces. Our bodies are not our enemies, they put us in motion and they both create and sustain life. The functions our bodies perform for us are too numerous and varied to list. Please vow that you will no longer fall victim to these images and help those around you to the road of self-love and acceptance.

*'let's stand up for ourselves, our values, our bodies, our lives'*

Advocate for freedom from body hatred and fight the billion dollar advertising, cosmetic, diet, entertainment and fashion industries. Let's stand up for ourselves, our values, our bodies and our lives. We must challenge ourselves, our culture and our children. The stakes are too high to back down. Lives are lost each year as beautiful, healthy young women starve themselves to death. Millions of us are suffering from depression and anxiety as we are bombarded with images of our "faults." It is time to change; change begins from within and radiates out - let's begin. Let's become fun, fearless, fighting females.

You are not who they see. "The Lord doesn't look at the things man looks at. Man looks at the outward appearance, but the Lord looks at the heart". [37] God judges not what is seen, but the unseen condition of our heart. He warns us not to spend time adorning ourselves with what will not count for eternity. I use to veil my heart, but this didn't hide it from God, it only obscured my vision causing me to believe I was unseen. When I first exposed my heart and turned to Christ I didn't like what I saw; the remnants of the flaws, wrinkles and blemishes of my former life. The clarification brought magnification to my shortcomings. Looking at my image did nothing to transform me; it simply discouraged me and limited me to myself. When I learnt to look deeper by the Spirit, I turned my focus from myself and towards Christ in me, the hope of Glory. When I allow myself to be transformed to the image of Christ, my worth is always increasing and my beauty is maturing and softening. The inner peace and rest is what will be noticed rather than the outward appearance.

What we all must understand is that our bodies do not belong to us. They are not ours to destroy; "Do you not know that your body is a temple of the Holy Spirit, who is in you, whom you have received from God? You are not your own; you were bought at a price. Therefore honour God with your body". [38] We are each loved by and individually important to God. He created us, He offered His son so we can have forgiveness, and He has given us stewardship over our bodies. Our ultimate help in healing is to turn to our loving Creator. By an act of our own will, we are to give our bodies back to the Lord, which means we need to change our ways of thinking. Our concept of our bodies is not the way God sees us. He sees you as His wonderfully made child. [39]

God thoughts are not our thoughts, neither are His ways our ways. Just as the heavens are higher than the earth, so are His ways higher than our ways. [40] This means through God's ways and abilities, He will help us to see ourselves the way He sees us. We can begin to heal through prayer and reading His Word to know what He says and can do for us. Allow God to heal your thinking,

**'God wants us to be able to love and be loved'**

your health, your body, and your spirit. Take advantage of the support of your loved ones and professionals whom the Lord has placed in your life. He loves you, wants you to be healed, and to come to Him for the miraculous healing He offers you. You are not what they see.

CS Lewis once wrote; "Does God want us to suffer? What if the answer to that question is 'yes'? You see, I'm not sure that God particularly wants us to be happy. I think he wants us to be able to love and be loved. He wants us to grow up. I suggest to you that it is because God loves us that he makes us the gift of suffering. Or to put it another way, pain is God's megaphone to rouse a deaf world. You see, we are like blocks of stone out of which the sculptor carves the forms of men. The blows of his chisel, which hurt us so much, are what make us perfect. We think our childish toys bring us all the happiness there is. And our nursery is the whole wide world. Something must drive us out of the nursery to the world of others, and that something is suffering."

God stands by us until we are free. He never forsakes us. God is the only one who is never repelled by the depth and length of our needs. Although God never excuses our sin and rebellion, He is fully aware of what drives our actions. When I was growing up, I had no idea why I was making some poor decisions, but God knew. Even though my rebellion was still sin, God's heart was full of compassion. Through loving chastisement, He continued to strive with me and waited patiently for me to leave my prison.

No matter how long we struggle, God is not giving up on us. Even if we have drained all the human resources around us dry, He is our inexhaustible well of living water. He allowed my life as a captive to grow more and more difficult, but only so I would get to a place of desperation in order to do what freedom in Christ requires. I am so thankful that God waited for me. The measures He took to woo me to liberty were excruciating at times, but they were more powerful evidences of His unfailing love than all the obvious blessings I

*'he waited patiently for me to leave my prison'*

*'I can now say that I have ascended from my own dark hell of hopelessness and into the light of recovery'*

could expound. Few truly know the unfailing love of God like the captive set free. I can now say that I have ascended from my own dark hell of hopelessness and into the light of recovery. I have allowed the Divine Surgeon to use His delicate surgical tools to restore my sight. The past blurriness has been focussed and the darkness dispersed. Christ has emerged from a wavy figure walking out of a desert mirage to become the touchable face of my best friend. My life has changed completely all thanks to God's saving grace. Now I am desperate for you and for your freedom. I hope that this book serves as a catalyst enabling you to join the unshackled multitude that is breaking free.

# chapter 9:

# abundant life

Ambition can be defined as an eager, strong and cherished desire to achieve something. The ability to dream and imagine is a unique gift from God. Ambition is the drive to actualize our dreams - where dreams are passive, ambition is active. Worldly ambition tends to focus on personal advancement and desire for power, rank, fame, wealth, and success. In contrast, Christian ambition is about serving those around us and concentrating on their development.

Before I became a Christian I had many worldly ambitions in both the academic and athletic fields.

My CV appears impressive; a straight A student at School, a good degree and over 10 years competing for Great Britain at an International level in 10k to Half Marathon events. However, my motivations to achieve were based on my desire for recognition. I was living in the performance acceptance trap striving for the approval of my parents and peers. I felt inadequate in myself, constantly questioned my worth and feared that I had little value. I believed that I had to perform well in whatever I did in order to earn the love of those around me.

I enjoyed most of my years of competing, but, despite winning many races I didn't respond to my triumphs with joy or satisfaction, but with added pressure, pressure to continue performing at that high level. My achievement in sport afforded me a small amount of self-esteem but the good feeling I had about my performance tended to be minimal as well as fleeting. Therefore, sport performance became a competition that I couldn't win. I had plenty of Gold medals but also had an empty, unfulfilled void inside.

Jonathan  Edwards, who is the World Record holder for the Triple Jump, became a full-time athlete in the belief that his preordained success would enable him to evangelize to an unbelieving world. The following is from an article from The Times in July 2007 titled  'I have never been happier,' says the man who won gold but lost God.

"I never doubted my belief in God for a single moment until I retired from sport," Jonathan says. "Faith was the reason that I decided to become a professional athlete, in the same way that it was fundamental to every decision I made. It was the foundation of my existence, the thing that made everything else make sense. It was not a sacrifice to refuse to compete on Sundays during my early career because that would imply that athletics was important in and of itself. It was not. It was always a means to an end: glorifying God. But when I retired, something happened that took me by complete surprise. I quickly realized that athletics was more important to my identity than I believed possible. I was the best in the world at what I did and suddenly that was not true *'it gave me a reason to get up in the morning and a reason to press on'*

any more. With one facet of my identity stripped away, I began to question the others and, from there, there was no stopping. The foundations of my world were slowly crumbling." I found this so sad to read and Jonathan claims that he no longer has a Christian faith. I can relate to Jonathan's identity crisis. At times of injury I fell apart because I didn't have a bigger plan or purpose to my life other than training and racing. Without my identity as an athlete to hide behind I felt insignificant and worthless and started questioning who I was, whether I really mattered and what life was all about. I felt aimless and directionless and at the time didn't have a relationship with God.

My dreams and ambitions became dangerous to my soul because they took hold of me. My dream had become a prized possession and by pursuing it, I had been slowly building my own personal tower to my personal heaven. It had me. It defined me. It motivated me. It guided me and directed me. It gave me a reason to get up in the morning and a reason to press on. I became convinced that life without the dream would be unthinkable and unliveable.

*'Unless you assume a God, the question of life's purpose is meaningless'*

An atheist called Bertrand Russell once said, "Unless you assume a God, the question of life's purpose is meaningless." The Bible confirms this; "For everything, absolutely everything, above and below, visible and invisible,... everything got started in him and finds its purpose in him". [41] The purpose of our lives is far greater than our own personal fulfilment, our peace of mind, or even our happiness. It is far greater than our family, our career, or even our wildest dreams and ambitions. If we want to discover why we were placed on this planet, we must begin with God. We were made by God and for God, and until we understand this, life will not make sense. It is only in God that we discover our origin, our identity, our meaning, our purpose, our significance, and our destiny. Every other path leads to a dead end. [42] My worldly ambitions have now been replaced by Godly ones. Whilst it isn't wrong to achieve in athletics and academia, the driving force in my life has now changed. I have been a world class athlete but my ambition now is to be a world class Christian who knows that I have been saved to serve and made for a mission.

God wants a family, and he created us to be a part of it. The entire Bible is the story of God building a family who will love him, honour him, and reign with him forever. When we place our faith in Christ, God becomes our Father, we become his children, other believers become our brothers and sisters, and the Church becomes our spiritual family. We are called to belong, not just to believe. We are created for community, fashioned for fellowship, and formed for a family, and none of us can fulfil God's purposes by ourselves. While our relationship to Christ is personal, God never intends it to be private.

Whenever a child is born, he or she automatically becomes a part of the universal family of human beings. However, that child also needs to become a member of a specific family to receive nurture and care and grow up healthy and strong. The same is true spiritually. As well as being part of God's universal family, we also need to become a member of a local expression of God's family. I believe that being a member of a thriving, growing, lively Church means being a vital organ of a living body; indispensible, interconnected and important. The Church is a body, not a building; an organism, not an organisation.

The Bible says a Christian without a church home is like an organ without a body, a sheep without a flock, or a child without a family. It is an unnatural state. It was because I realized the importance of becoming planted in God's house that I moved to Bradford to join The Abundant Life Church (ALC). I had always lived, studied and worked in the South of England but I felt God tell me to uproot geographically to the North to become part of this new church family. It was a massive leap of faith and a brave step because I had no job waiting, no friends and no knowledge of that part of the country. I am now very glad that I was obedient to God's instructions because vital friendships have been formed and doors have opened that otherwise would not have. God's big dot to dot for my life is taking shape.

When I was young, my experience had been that Church was boring, especially the sermons. The messages did not relate to my life. It is amazing how Churches are able to take the most exciting book in the world and bore people to tears with it. The uninspiring, mind-numbing, dreary and dull preachers that I had heard caused me to think that God was boring. However, once I arrived at ALC, I found that God's word could be communicated in a positive, practical, encouraging and interesting way. I realized that a sermon does not need to be boring to be biblical, and it doesn't have to be dry to be doctrinal.

Some pastors criticize "life application" preaching as shallow, simplistic, and inferior. To them, the only real preaching is doctrinal preaching. However, I want to hear something on a Sunday that I can apply on a Monday. In my opinion, we need fewer "ought-to" sermons and more "how-to" sermons. The deepest kind of teaching is that which makes a difference in people's day to day lives. As D.L Moody once said "The Bible was not given to increase our knowledge, but to change our lives." A teacher is one who trains God's people in the truth and teaches others to do so. It is essential that the Church is careful whom they allow to preach. I know that ALC is selective about who they permit on the platform, and rightly so. We are to obey

*'the Bible was not given to increase our knowledge, but to change our lives'*

our spiritual leaders and submit to them, and in return they should be constantly keeping watch over our souls and guarding our spiritual welfare, as men who will have to render an account of their trust. The pastor of a Church sets the tone and atmosphere of the congregation. I have been to some Churches where the pastor's cold demeanour and lack of personal warmth has guaranteed my not returning. A pastor must be loving and lead by example. John Maxwell states that leadership is influence and the ability to obtain followers. His favourite leadership proverb is: He who think he leadeth and hath no one following him is only taking a walk! [43] ALC has some phenomenal leaders who inspire me to reach greater heights. By becoming part of the church family at ALC I have been able to move 'it is easy to fool ourselves into thinking we are mature if there is no one to challenge us'

out of self-centred isolation. I have decided to dedicate a year of my life to God and am currently on the ALC Pastoral Leadership Academy. This is giving me the opportunity to increase my theoretical knowledge of the Bible under the tuition of some very wise teachers, and also to put into practice what I am learning by serving in the church. The church family is helping me develop spiritual muscle. You will never grow to maturity just by attending worship services and being a passive spectator. Only participation in the full life of the church builds spiritual muscle. Isolation breeds deceitfulness; it is easy to fool ourselves into thinking we are mature if there is no one to challenge us. Real maturity shows up in relationships. I have grown faster and stronger by learning from others and being accountable to them. I am certainly not immune to temptation. Given the right situation, I am capable of backsliding. God knows this, so he has assigned us as individuals the responsibility of keeping each other on track.

God has five purposes for our lives. [44] These include loving God, loving others, sharing God's message, identifying with his church and growing in maturity. One of the events in the summer Olympics is the pentathlon. It is composed of five events: pistol shooting, fencing, horseback, riding, running, and swimming. The pentathlete's goal is to succeed in all five areas, not just one or two. Our individual lives are a pentathlon of the five aforementioned purposes which must be kept in balance.

The first purpose is to love the Lord with all our heart, and this is done by magnifying God with our worship. Worship is not restricted to music, our whole life should be a seamless act of worship. Surrendering to God is the heart of worship. The second purpose is to love our neighbour. The word we use to describe this purpose is ministry. The Church exists to minister to people. Ministry is demonstrating God's love to others by meeting their needs and healing their hurts in the name of Jesus. The Church is to minster to all kinds of needs: spiritual, emotional, relational, and physical.

"The most miserable people in the world are the people who are self-centred, who don't do anything for anybody except themselves. They are centres of misery with no exceptions. On the contrary, the happiest people are the people who deliberately take on themselves the sorrows and troubles of others. Their hearts sing with a strange wild joy, automatically and with no exceptions. We are structured for the outgoingness of the love of the Kingdom. It is our native land." [45]

I used to be very inverted and centred on myself, preoccupied with my rights, my life, my liberty, and my pursuit of happiness. In some places, religion has become a means toward self-realisation with the interest being on self-esteem, self-fulfilment, and self-identity. However, I have found that when A helps B, A is set free. By stopping my navel gazing, allowing my mess to become my message and using my tests to contribute to my testimony I hope to bind up the broken-hearted, set many

*'I use to be very inverted and centred on myself, preoccupied with my rights, my life, my liberty, and my pursuit of happiness'*

*'when A helps B,
A is set free'*

captives free, and release from darkness the prisoners. I have been helped to shed my painful past and move into a productive future and would like to help others do the same. I was comforted when I was in trouble so that I could share that same comfort with others in trouble[46]. The spiritual comfort I received was not given for my use alone; it, like all the gifts of God, was given so that I may distribute it and become an instrument of help to others. I am throwing off everything that hinders and the sin that so easily entangles, and intend to run with perseverance the new race marked out for me. You've all been to the stadium and seen the athletes race. Everyone runs; one wins. We also need to run to win. All good athletes train hard, but they do it for a gold medal that tarnishes and fades. I have many gold medals from my years of competing, but now I am after one that is gold eternally. After we have been good and faithful servants on this earth I look forward to seeing you on the podium in heaven with your medal around your neck.

# chapter 10:

# my fairytale ending

*"A dream is a wish your heart makes
  when it's fast asleep"*

*From Cinderella*

As a child I loved fairytales and reading stories of whimsical wonder and far-fetched fantasy. I would let my imagination take flight as I pictured the beautiful helpless princess, the handsome brave prince who would rescue her and, of course, the token wicked stepmother who tried to thwart their happiness. I use to sing and tell stories with my lips that betrayed the longings of my heart.

My eating disorder had become the dark fortress of my own construction. I had become the architect of my own demise. I would imagine what it would be like to be rescued by a love bigger and stronger than any of my chains; a love capable of navigating the deep emotional moats surrounding my life; a love brave enough to face off any dragon threatening my heart and a love able to break through the isolation of walls I had built to keep others at bay. How remarkable to discover that while I waited in dark slumber, a lover, noble beyond compare, fought through every barrier with the burning desire to awaken me with a kiss. God is the only King of the universe and His Son, Jesus, the original crown Prince, is the ultimate redeemer of all captive beauties. I have been woken from my passing nightmare and forever transported into my dream.

God knows the desires of my heart because he put them there in the first place. I have always wanted to be a bride, then a great wife and mother. However, before I could love my future husband with all my heart, I had to learn to love myself, because a proper self love is the basis for a healthy relationship. I have heard it said that 'What we be begins with me.' Every we includes a me and whatever is inside of me I bring to a relationship. If I am broken and hurting, with defences up, and trust issues, then I will bring this to a partnership. We can't expect men to complete and fix us because only God can do this. In a healthy marriage, you need two secure individuals coming together so that their combinational strength is greater than the sum of its two parts. 'Two people can accomplish more than twice as much as one; they get a better return for their labour. If one person falls, the other can reach out and help. But people who are alone when they fall are in real trouble. And on a cold night, two under the same blanket can gain warmth from each other. But how can one be

> *'God knows the desires of my heart because he put them there in the first place'*

warm alone? [47] 'Marriage, in its right time, offers the advantages of both synergy and unity. God had to finish his work of restoration in me before he could introduce me to my future husband.

I was not looking for a relationship, but God knew when I was ready to commit to loving, honouring and respecting my future husband, and it was then that my knight in shining armour came to capture my heart so that he could sweep me away.

The Abundant Life Church is spiritually deep and numerically large, with a congregation of about 2000. It is easy to go unnoticed, but God shone a spotlight down on me and highlighted my presence to a gentleman called Lewis. God said to Lewis, "That is the woman you are going to marry. Pursue her, woo her, be gentle with her and give her your heart. Love her like she has never been loved before."

Lewis was certainly not backwards in coming forwards and stated his intentions very clearly right from the beginning. It would be dignified and tidy if couples always fell for each other at precisely the same moment, if they saw each other and ZING BAM BOOM love hit them both between the eyes. However, Lewis had a mini mission to get me to reciprocate, but after some cunning manoeuvres I too had the revelation that we were meant to be together forever. I had found my soul mate and our heart connection is unreal. We speak the same love languages and I feel so safe, secure, happy and contented in his company. 'A person standing alone can be attacked and defeated, but two can stand back-to-back and conquer. Three are even better, for a triple-braided cord is not easily broken.[48]' God is certainly at the centre of our relationship and makes up the third strand.

Lewis is a very precious gift. He has restored my faith in men and, towering above me at 6'4", he is my BFG! (Big Friendly Giant) He has the largest heart of anyone I have known and is so kind and selfless. Due to my past encounters with men I have had a great fear of letting my guard down but I know that I can trust Lewis implicitly. He has given me the freedom to express myself

'Whatever we embrace as truth determines our destiny'

without fear, and has allowed me to feel safe when I make myself vulnerable. By the end of this year I will be his bride and my dreams are coming true.

Throughout my life, I have had many names, labels and roles attached to me that had become part of my identity. Whatever we embrace as truth determines our destiny. It is time to leave behind the lies and embrace the facts in God's word about who we really are.

I mentioned in the first chapter the meaning of my names and that I didn't feel that I was worthy of their descriptions. Alison is a Scottish name which means noble. Noble can be defined as possessing outstanding qualities and of high birth or exalted rank. Rather than seeing myself as a miserable slug, I now know that I am a princess warrior daughter of the King most High, precious, priceless and prized by God. Catharine, on the other hand means pure; clean, not contaminated, innocent and free from taint or defilement. I acknowledge that I felt dirty, contaminated and defiled but thank God for the life of his Son given to make me white as snow. I no longer feel vulnerable, naked, shamed and afraid as I am now clothed in the honour, strength, mystery and nobility that God has hidden in the feminine form.

"A good, capable, intelligent, noble and virtuous woman is hard to find. She is far more precious than jewels and her value is far above rubies, diamonds or pearls. The heart of her husband trusts in her confidently and relies on and believes in her securely. She comforts, encourages and does him only good as long as there is life within her... She is clothed with strength and dignity; she can laugh at the days to come. She speaks with wisdom, and faithful instruction is on her tongue. She watches over the affairs of her household and does not eat the bread of idleness. Her children arise and call her blessed; her husband also, and he praises her: 'Many women do noble things, but you surpass them all.' Charm is deceptive, and beauty is fleeting; but a woman who fears the Lord is to be praised."

'I have given up the desire to win and instead want to give my time and energy to ensure others have a safe journey'

The aforementioned description is of the woman in Proverbs 31. She seems so perfect, ideal and almost unbelievable. However, she was no fantasy, and a closer look at her life reveals that she possesses qualities that I, as a young woman eager to please God, can develop and apply in my life. Alison means noble and the Proverbs 31 woman was noble. I want to cultivate her beautiful qualities in my life, and in order for these to permeate every area and relationship like coloured threads in a tapestry I have to continually work on my character.

Our character is the result of the habits in our life and furthermore our destiny is dependent upon our character. "Character is who you are when no one is looking." [50] It is the real you, the private you, who you are without the mask or charade. Character is also something that is not developed overnight. It takes diligence and commitment to be more Christ-like. "The fruit of the Spirit is love, joy, peace, patience, kindness, goodness, faithfulness, gentleness and self-control." [51] These nine fruits of the Spirit are the qualities that I believe we need to develop in our lives if we want to be known as young women of character. And although they are all important, the number one quality of good character is LOVE. "A virtuous, noble and worthy wife, earnest and strong in character, is a crowning joy to her husband." [52] I want to be the best wife I can be to Lewis, the finest most dependable friend, the greatest mother, and reliable, trustworthy, truthful and loyal to everyone God places in my world. "He who travels the road best is he who makes the road smoother for those who will follow." I am now more interested in making the road easier, smoother and safer for other travellers, than finishing first or fastest. I have given up the desire to win and instead want to give my time and energy to ensure others have a safe journey.

I truly believe that people need my story and they need yours too. Never be tempted to reduce 'Once upon a time...' to only fairy tale settings. Once upon a time, you were planned, designed, conceived and arrived on the planet in the perfect timing and purpose of Almighty God. Life is a journey. It has a beginning and an end, and everything that happens along the way becomes the fabric of your story. Unfortunately many people fail to negotiate life or live within the safe parameters of wisdom, and they end up with a tale of distance travelled that is less successful and fulfilling than was intended. This was the case in my life due to both my own bad choices and also circumstances imposed on me which were beyond my control. However, the second half of my story is going to be different because I have connected to and framed my life with the more successful principles of right living.

Whatever the scenario, your story and experience is valuable, and has the capacity to make a difference in this world. Your life has the amazing ability and potential to touch countless people. All of us have negatives to deal with, but dealt with and overcome, they become powerful tools that can bring inspiration, healing, deliverance and restoration to others. I hope that my story of overcoming has been a source of blessing to you. I'm sure that as you turned the pages, other women struggling with similar issues to those I battled with came to your mind. I would encourage you to give them a copy of this book because I believe that my testimony of Christ at work in me can bring wisdom, clarity, hope and freedom to them too.

We are all influencing and being influenced by others. Every one of us continually exerts influence either to heal, to bless, to leave marks of beauty; or to wound, to hurt, to poison, or to stain other lives. I hope that this book has had a positive influence on you and in the words of John Maxwell...

*My life shall touch a dozen lives*
*Before this day is done.*
*Leave countless marks of good or ill,*
*E'er sets the evening sun.*

*This, the wish I always wish,*
*The prayer I always pray*
*Lord, may my life help others' lives*
*It touches by the way.*

I would like to finish with some wise words from Nelson Mandela; "Our deepest fear is not that we are inadequate. Our deepest fear is that we are powerful beyond measure. It is our light, not our darkness, that most frightens us. We ask ourselves 'Who am I to be brilliant, gorgeous, talented and fabulous?' Actually, who are you not to be? You are a child of God. Your playing small doesn't serve anyone in the world. There's nothing enlightening about shrinking so that other people won't feel insecure around you. We are all meant to shine, as children do. We are born to manifest the glory of God that is within us. It is not just in some of us; it is in all of us. And as we let our own light shine we unconsciously give other people permission to do the same. As we are liberated from our own fear, our presence automatically liberates others"

'Our deepest fear is not that we are inadequate. Our deepest fear is that we are powerful beyond measure'

We grow great by dreams... some of us let these great dreams die, but others nourish and protect them; nurse them through bad days till they bring sunshine and light which comes always to those who sincerely hope that their dreams come true. This book is dedicated to you, to women young and old who long to dream but have forgotten how. I pray that the words on these pages reawakened and strengthened the dream in your heart. It is my prayer that you will make the truths of God's Word your own and chase away every shadowy memory, fear or nightmare that stands between you and joy unspeakable.

# thank you

## I would like to say a big thank you to...

**God**, my heavenly Father, who lovingly created me, considers me individually important and valuable, and gives my life a purpose and meaning. May your precious Word always be flesh in my life so others may glimpse your beauty.

**Jesus**, my ultimate Prince and Saviour, who made the ultimate sacrifice by dying for me to give me freedom, forgiveness and favour. My limited words and actions could never adequately express the depth of my gratitude and affection.

**The Holy Spirit**, my comforter, counsellor, and conscience, who has transformed me from within.

**Lewis**, my future husband, for pursuing me, for being my knight in shining armour, for giving me your heart in all its entirety, and for being the most selfless and loving man I know. You cause me to simply blossom!

My parents **Alan** and **Jean**, for bringing me into this world and for giving me the best you could. Thank you for the support, and sacrifices you have made over the years.

**John** and **Trish Edwards** for being such fantastic role models and encouraging me in my writing. I look forward to our journey ahead working together in Walking Free Ministries. I know that many lives around the world are going to be touched and transformed as we share our stories and give hope and inspiration to those in need.

My travelling companions, who shall remain nameless, but you know who you are. I am indebted to you for your precious treasured friendship, faithful prayers and for the tears you have shed on my behalf when I was too numb to cry.

**Mark** and **Neil** for your design and technical expertise and for making it possible to meet publication deadlines.

**Helen Allen** for your editorial assistance in reading through my first draft and for your gentle correction and constructive criticism.

# useful contact information

For further information about eating disorders, contact your GP or any of the following recommended organisations. For further information about eating disorders, contact your GP or any of the following recommended organisations.

# anorexia and bulimia care

ABC is a national (within the UK) Christian charity working to support all those who suffer because of eating disorders and their associated problems.

Whether you are a sufferer yourself, or are trying to support someone else, ABC aim to provide help, advice and assistance to help you.

For sufferers ABC can offer email and telephone support, various resources to help move towards recovery and a befriending scheme, where recovered sufferers offer one to one friendship and support to help the sufferer on the road to recovery. Part of ABC is specifically to offer support for parents and carers. ACHE (Anorexic Children, Help and Encouragement) can offer resources, advice, support and a chance to share experiences with others who have been through the same. ABC can also offer training for professional groups, and resources for use in preventative schemes in schools, colleges and universities.

*Website: www.anorexiabulimiacare.co.uk*
*Email: help@anorexiabulimiacare.co.uk*
*Tel: (0) 1462 423 351*

# *beat*

Beating Eating Disorders

Beat formally known as the Eating Disorder Association (EDA) is a national charity (Registered Charity No. 801343) based in the UK providing information, help and support for people affected by eating disorders and, in particular, anorexia and bulimia nervosa. beat's vision is that eating disorders will be beaten.

## Beat's aims are:

To change the way everyone thinks and talks about eating disorders. To improve the way services and treatment are provided. And to help anyone believe that their eating disorder can be beaten.

## They do this by:

Challenging the stereotypes and stigma that people with eating disorders face campaigning for better services and treatment Providing information, support and encouragement to seek treatment and recovery.

## Adult Helpline: 0845 6341414

*Mon-Fri: 10:30-18:30, Sat: 13:00- 16:30*
*Email: help@b-eat.co.uk*

## Youth Helpline (under 25): 0845 6347650

*Mon-Fri: 16:30-20:30, Sat: 13:00-16:30*
*Email: fyp@b-eat.co.uk*

# mercy

Mercy Ministries is a national non-profit organisation dedicated to providing homes and care, free of charge, for young women suffering the effects of eating disorders, self harm, abuse, depression, unplanned pregnancies and other life controlling issues.

Mercy Ministries provides a 6 month structured residential based programme that includes life-skills training, Equine Assisted Therapy and professional counselling based on Christian principles.

Mercy provides a holistic programme that addresses all aspects of a young woman's well being; physical, spiritual and emotional. Their goal is to have each young woman not only complete the programme but also discover the purpose for her life and bring value to her community as a productive citizen.

## Who they help

Mercy Ministries UK helps young women between the ages of 16-28, who display a sincere desire to change. Young women come to Mercy Ministries suffering the effects of eating disorders, self harm, abuse, depression, unplanned pregnancies and other life controlling issues.

## Mercy Ministries UK

*Website: www.mercyministries.co.uk*
*Tel: 01535 642042*
*Email: info@mercyministries.co.uk*
*Mercy Ministries of America*
*Tel: (615) 8316987*
*Website: www.mercyministries.com*

# national centre for eating disorders

The National Centre For Eating Disorders, established in 1984, is an independent organisation set up to provide solutions for all eating problems, compulsive or "binge" eating, failed or "yo-yo" dieting, bulimia and anorexia. Their services include:

## Counselling

State of the art treatment services for all the eating problems. Their therapists can provide one-to one personal therapy, group counselling and telephone counselling. They also offer help and support to the family and friends of those who are in eating distress.

## Professional Training

The National Centre now offers the only complete Training Course in Treatment skills for eating disorders in the UK, providing a unique self

employment opportunity for people who wish to work full time or part time in this field.
Website: www.eating-disorders.org.uk
Tel: 0845 838 2040

# *overeaters anonymous*

Overeaters Anonymous is a fellowship of individuals who, through shared experience, strength and hope, are recovering from compulsive overeating. They welcome everyone who wants to stop eating compulsively. There are no dues or fees for members; they are self-supporting through their own contributions, neither soliciting nor accepting outside donations. OA is not affiliated with any public or private organization, political movement, ideology or religious doctrine; they take no position on outside issues. Their primary purpose is to abstain from compulsive overeating and to carry this message of recovery to those who still suffer.

*Website: www.oagb.org.uk*
*Address: PO Box 19*
*Stretford, Manchester, M32 6EB*
*Tel: 07000 784 985*

# *bibliography*

1   Mother Teresa

2   Theodore Roosevelt

3   J. McDowell, See Yourself as God Sees You (Alpha Publishing, 1999)

4   P. Scanlon, I Am Not My Father (Abundant Life Publishing, 2007)

5   Gary Chapman, The Five Love Languages (Northfield Publishing Chicago, 2004)

6   Margo Maine, Father Hunger

7   John & Stasi Eldredge, Captivating (Thomas Neson, Inc, 2005) p61

8   L. Bevere, Kissed the Girls and Made Them Cry (Thomas Nelson Publishers, Nashville, 2002) p185

9   A.G.Cole, Body and Soul: Eating Disorders as a Re-enactment of Sexual Abuse paper. (The Horsham Clinic, Amber, Pennsylvania, November 1992) p12

10  H. Wilkinson, Beyond Chaotic Eating (Roper Penberthy Publishing Ltd, Horsham, 2001)

11  H. Wilkinson, Beyond Chaotic Eating (Roper Penberthy Publishing Ltd, Horsham, 2001)

12  P. Lambley, How to Survive Anorexia (Frederick Muller, London, 1983), p125

13  Psalm 109:22-24, 26 (The Message Bible)

14  M. Dana and M. Laurence, Women's Secret Disorder (Grafton, London, 1998)

15  M. Lawrence and M. Dana, Fighting Food, (Penguin, London, 1990) p48

16  Isaiah 55:1-2

17  RS Weinberg, D Gould. Foundations of Sport & Exercise Psychology. (Champaign, IL: Human Kinetics Publishers, Inc. 2003)

18  D Mandel. Turn on your Inner Light: Fitness for Body, Mind and Soul. (NY: Busy Bee Group. 2003)

19  Inaba DS, Cohen WE, Holstein ME. Uppers, Downers, All Arounders: Physical and Mental Effects of Psychoactive Drugs. (Oregan: CNS Publications, Inc. 1997)

20  1 Timothy 4:8

21  Ezekiel 36:26-27

22  www.alpha.org

23  www.mercyministries.com

24  Proverbs 27:6

25  Romans 7:14

26  Galatians 6:7

27  James 4:17

28  2 Timothy 3:16

29  Hebrews 12:6

30  Mary Pytches, A Child no More.

31  C.A.Poggi, Many Thanks for the Things in My
    Life, Peter Pauper Press Inc, New York, 1999

32  Genesis. 2:7

33  Philippians 4:6-7

34  John 10:10

35  1 Peter 5:8

36  Ephesians 6:10-20

37  1 Samuel 16:7

38  1 Corinthians 6:20

39  Psalm 139:13-14

40  Isaiah 55:8-9

41  Colossians 1:16

42  Rick Warren, The Purpose Driven Life
    (Zondervan, 2002)

43  John C Maxwell, Developing The Leader
    Within You  (Thomas Nelson Publishers,
    Nashville, 1993)

44  Rick Warren, The Purpose Driven Life
    (Zondervan, 2002)

45  E. Stanley Jones, The Unshakeable Kingdom
    and the Unchanging Person

46  2 Corinthians 1:4

47  Ecclesiastes 4:9-11

48  Ecclesiastes 4:12

49  L. Bevere, Kissed the Girls and Made Them
    Cry (Thomas Nelson Publishers, Nashville,
    2002) p191

50  D.L. Moody

51  Galatians 5:22

52  Proverbs 12:4